# 5 PROFIT ENGINES

## OF A

## SUCCESSFUL BARIATRIC SURGERY PRACTICE

Your Blueprint for Building an
Enjoyable Business that Creates Healthy
Patients and a Healthy Bottom Line

# KAROL H. CLARK

# 5 Profit Engines of a Successful Bariatric Surgery Practice

*Your Blueprint for Building an Enjoyable Business that Creates Healthy Patients and a Healthy Bottom Line*

## Karol H. Clark

### 3 – Time #1 Best-Selling Author

For additional Free resources and training, go to
www.WeightLossPracticeBuilder.com

© 2017 Karol H. Clark, MSN, RN

Published by Adriel Publishing

FIRST EDITION

Published in the U.S.A.

ISBN: 978-1-939998-10-1

www.WeightLossPracticeBuilder.com

Karol can be reached at
Karol@WeightLossPracticeBuilder.com
or through her business sites at
www.WeightLossPracticeBuilder.com
and
www.YourBestSellerBook.com

## Dedication

This book is dedicated to my visionary and caring husband, Tom, and all of the healthcare professionals who work tirelessly to improve the health of their overweight patients so they can live longer lives and enjoy life to the fullest.

And to our loyal, smart, dedicated, caring and creative team that believes in our mission and drives success for the business and the people we serve every day. Cat, Dawn, Cat (yes we have 2 Cat's), Dani, Tina, Jessica, Arlyne and Desiree – we are blessed to have you in our lives and on our team! Thank you for all you do!

# Contents

## About This Book

Every bariatric surgeon and bariatric program has different needs. This book was written for both independent bariatric surgeons and hospital based programs. The information is applicable in nearly every bariatric surgery setting.

Some of you may be interested in all of the content and I say 'go for it'! For others, you may have some aspects outlined in this book running at top speed and only want assistance with one or two of the profit engines or practice management and marketing sections. That's great too! The information is intended to provide you with new ideas and implementation plans so you can shorten your learning curve. This results in quicker implementation and greater profitability for your business.

The bonus chapters were written based upon feedback from bariatric surgeons who have specifically requested assistance with those topics. Bottom line, your success is my goal. I am ALWAYS committed to a positive return on investment (ROI) whether you just read this book, take one or more of my courses or invest in an on-site evaluation or VIP immersion weekend for quicker implementation. As long as you remain coachable and implement what is taught, I am willing to continue to work with you until you have a full return on your investment.

I have been there and can relate to the unique needs of bariatric surgeons (I am married to one), weight loss surgery programs and the patients they serve. I fully understand the need for profitability, efficient systems, improved long-term patient outcomes and overall enjoyment for all involved. I wrote this book in order to help bariatric surgeons enjoy their practice more as well as earn more while keeping the focus of their patients and their improved outcomes at heart.

I am interested in your feedback and I welcome a 30 minute free strategy session with you to get you 'unstuck' and moving towards your short and long-term goals. Please share your thoughts and your success with me and/or let me know if you desire an outcome oriented strategy session. I can be reached at Karol@WeightLossPracticeBuilder.com or you can schedule directly at www.smarturl.it/bookkarol

# Introduction

I have had a number of consulting conversations with bariatric surgeons at various stages in their career. I am not sure where you are in your journey, but I know that a number of emotions go hand in hand with creating and running a bariatric surgery practice. Such emotions occur whether you are self-employed or employed by a larger health system. These emotions range from excitement, pride, confidence, appreciation and enjoyment to fear, exhaustion, frustration, burn out and depression. It is my mission to help surgeons, administrators and support staff to build a profitable bariatric surgery program so they worry less, achieve more, have outstanding patient outcomes and enjoy the process along the way.

Although the title can be misleading, this book is not just about the money (albeit very important for you and your patients). This book is about creating a business that attracts your ideal patients, improves their outcomes and is sustainable so you have peace of mind that systems are in place for outstanding customer service and a positive bottom line. It is about serving others in a predictable and personalized way that sets you apart from your competition and brings enjoyment to your career.

Weight Loss Practice Builder and this book came about because I was approached by various bariatric surgeons, bariatricians, health systems, medical corporations and nutritional corporations regarding the comprehensive weight loss business that my husband and I had built in Newport News, Virginia. They wanted to know if it was a 'chain' or if we had thought of franchising. Franchising is not particularly something we are interested in doing at this time. However, I knew I was interested in working one on one with such individuals so they could duplicate our success, help more patients and experience more enjoyment in their business. I hope this book helps you do the same!

There is no doubt that now is an exciting time to have a weight loss surgery program. The number of primary weight loss surgery procedures continues to trend upward and more surgeons are becoming fellowship trained than those that are retiring.[1] In addition, it seems as if new bariatric surgery programs are popping up across the United States to better serve the more than 18 million + adults who qualify and could benefit from treatment. Especially since only about 1% of this demographic actually undergoes weight loss surgery, which has been shown to be an effective treatment of morbid obesity and the co-morbidities that tend to be associated with this recognized disease.[2]

To help ensure quality of care and adherence to standards along with attracting new patients, most of the hospitals with bariatric surgery programs are accredited as a Bariatric Center of Excellence. This is completed by at least one of the two current agencies that inspect the facility, collect data and accredits the hospital with this designation. Yet training for how to create a high quality comprehensive bariatric surgery program that exceeds patient expectations, improves their long term outcomes and has sustainable profitability is difficult to find (especially the profitability part...which most clinicians don't like to openly discuss).

I would be remiss not to mention the many stumbling blocks that are occurring in healthcare today. The negative realities of dwindling reimbursement, managed care, higher insurance premiums, rising overhead, poor profit margins and having to do more with less are unsettling at best. However, there are proven ways to combat each so you can avoid financial instability of your bariatric surgery program as well as physician/staff burnout.

Whether you are building a weight loss surgery practice from the ground up or striving to grow your existing program, you are about to learn a formula that will help you meet or exceed industry standards and ensure the long term viability of your program. All while improving patient outcomes, enhancing your bottom line and resulting in more enjoyment and satisfaction for your surgeons, your employees and your patients. So let's get started!

## Chapter 1:

## Top Trends in Weight Loss Surgery
## (Staying Ahead of the Curve)

Before we get to the specifics of how to build, manage and market your successful bariatric surgery program, it's important to briefly review obesity as it is understood today along with some documented trends and intuitive personal predictions. Staying ahead of the curve (and your competition) depends upon understanding trends of what the future may hold so you can proactively plan and prepare adequately.

As you know, obesity was officially recognized as a disease by the American Medical Association in 2013.[3] Although some still debate this designation, the reality remains that there is more to being overweight than a lack of willpower and genetics. This disease necessitates treatment and for many who meet surgical criteria, weight loss surgery is a lifesaving proposition.

*Staying ahead of the curve (and your competition) depends upon understanding trends of what the future may hold so you can proactively plan and prepare adequately.*

This designation helped to open the door to additional research, coordination of care and improved resources. However, this designation does not negate the fact that weight loss requires much work and dedication to integrate healthier habits in order to ensure short and long term weight loss results. This is an important tenet to understand and an integral message for every bariatric surgery program to impart to their weight loss surgery patients. As anyone in the field understands, weight loss surgery is a tool to help you lose weight. However, you must understand how to use your tool properly to ensure long term success. It is not the 'magic bullet' as some desire it to be.

As with any specialty, weight loss surgery has evolved over the years through research, experience and technical advancement. At the time this book was written, the American Society for Metabolic and Bariatric Surgery (ASMBS) has published a report that supports the following procedures as treatment for obesity.

- Laparoscopic Roux-en-Y Gastric Bypass

- Duodenal Switch

- Sleeve Gastrectomy

- Adjustable Gastric Banding

- Bariatric Reoperative Procedures

- Vertical Banded Gastroplasty*

- Open procedures as deemed appropriate by the surgeon

*As of 2016 Vertically Banded Gastroplasty was under review by the ASMBS Pathway for Approval of New Devices and Procedures Committee[4]

While every expert surgeon has their operative preference, these are the supported procedures by the governing body for bariatric surgery most choose from as they discuss options with their patients. The surgery is one (albeit extremely important) part of the overall bariatric surgery journey. Educational preparation before surgery, *engaging* ongoing support, patient motivation/compliance, excellent clinical care, healthy habit formation and long term counseling/education are what drive overall success. Each of these needs to be addressed in any comprehensive bariatric surgery program along with proper patient selection prior to surgery.

Now let's get to the trends!

## Karol's Top Trends in Weight Loss Surgery

| | |
|---|---|
| Trend #1 | Gastric Sleeve will Continue to be the Primary Bariatric Procedure Performed and the Total Number of Procedures will Rise and then Stabilize Over the Next 10 Years |
| Trend #2 | Continued Dwindling of Physician Reimbursement & Higher Premiums for Patients |
| Trend #3 | Increase in Cash Pay Surgery (with the Proper Mindset & Marketing Plan) |
| Trend #4 | Need for Additional Revenue Streams |
| Trend #5 | Increase in Patient/Family Expectations |
| Trend #6 | Increasingly Difficult Long-Term Follow-Up |

Trend #7       Increased Program Competition/
Survival of the Fittest

**Trend #1: Gastric Sleeve will Continue to be the Primary Bariatric Procedure Performed and the Total Number of Procedures will Rise and then Stabilize Over the Next 10 Years**

As you can see from the table below, the latest weight loss surgery statistics indicate a rise of weight loss surgery procedures of close to 20% from 2011 to 2015.[5] You can also see that the Gastric Sleeve has been the top procedure of choice since 2013. This is likely due to the fact that it is a less invasive procedure that provides good overall weight loss results and less long term complications. Some studies show an average weight loss of 60% of excess weight.[6] While other studies show weight loss with the Gastric Sleeve at a higher percentage.[7]

# Estimate of Bariatric Surgery Numbers, 2011-2015

Published July 2016

|  | 2011 | 2012 | 2013 | 2014 | 2015 |
|---|---|---|---|---|---|
| Total | 158,000 | 173,000 | 179,000 | 193,000 | 196,000 |
| RNY | 36.7% | 37.5% | 34.2% | 26.8% | 23.1% |
| Band | 35.4% | 20.2% | 14% | 9.5% | 5.7% |
| Sleeve | 17.8% | 33% | 42.1% | 51.7% | 53.8% |
| BPD/DS | 0.9% | 1% | 1% | 0.4% | 0.6% |
| Revisions | 6% | 6% | 6% | 11.5% | 13.6% |
| Other | 3.2% | 2.3% | 2.7% | 0.1% | 3.2% |
| Balloons |  |  |  |  | ~700 cases |
| V-Bloc |  |  |  |  | 18 cases |

ASMBS total bariatric procedures numbers from 2011, 2012, 2013, 2014 and 2015 are based on the best estimation from available data (BOLD, ASC/MBSAQIP, National Inpatient Sample data and outpatient estimations).

I predict that the number of overall primary weight loss surgeries will continue to increase. This is due to continued demand for weight loss surgery, low penetration of the population of candidates that meet criteria for surgery, positive outcomes, lower complication rates, improving economy (willingness to pay cash as necessary for some patients) and easier access to quality bariatric surgery programs. However, with the current state of healthcare coverage, higher premiums and less coverage for such elective procedures, I predict that the overall number of procedures will stabilize over the next 10 years.

## Trend #2: Continued Dwindling Physician Reimbursement & Higher Premiums for Patients

As with many specialties, physician reimbursement is on the decline within the bariatric field. A great influence is the Affordable Care Act and the federal government lowering Medicare reimbursement rates. When this happens, private insurance companies tend to follow suit. Not only are they lowering physician reimbursement rates, but the federal government is also moving towards a flat reimbursement rate regardless of the complexity of the patient's condition.[8] This ultimately affects payment for the hospital and the physician. It can also negatively affect patient care. You see, with this model, in order to remain solvent, the volume of visits/procedures needs to increase in the same amount of time. Thus, there is less time to spend with patients and potentially higher complications/ readmission rates among other negative outcomes. As an end result, stress overtakes the enjoyment of caring for patients (which has already happened in many facets of healthcare) and contributes to burnout which negatively affects the quality as well.

As you can see from the table below, at a comprehensive bariatric surgery private practice in Virginia, the physician reimbursement for 2 common procedures has not only gone down, but the gap between private insurance reimbursement and governmental healthcare is beginning to disappear. This is in addition to bundling some procedures together instead of reimbursing separately such as the Gastric Sleeve (CPT 43775) and Hiatal Hernia Repair (47100,51) when completed during the same surgical event.

---

**2017 Reimbursement Rates for an Independent Virginia Bariatric Surgery Practice**

* Average Reimbursement Sleeve Gastrectomy Commercial: $1,200.00

* Average Reimbursement Sleeve Gastrectomy Medicare[9]: $1,147.00

* Average Reimbursement Liver Biopsy Commercial: $436.11

* Average Reimbursement Liver Biopsy Medicare: $487.12

---

In addition to dwindling reimbursement for physicians, patient premiums and co-pays continue to rise.[10] This can be a significant deterrent to follow-up care beyond the global period and creates challenges for proper follow-up and obtaining the required long-term data.

## Trend #3: Increase in Cash Pay Surgery (with the Proper Mindset & Marketing Plan)

Implementing a cash pay weight loss surgery option for your patients can be a very positive game changer for your bariatric surgery program. There is a sub-population of patients seeking such services but they come with specific expectations (and often a bit more determination and motivation). Cash pay services in a variety of specialties is becoming much more common. These include plastic surgery/aesthetics, orthopedic services and even concierge family practice settings.

Here are a few important cash pay bariatric surgery insights that I have recorded while managing a bariatric surgery practice that currently has a self-pay rate of 28.6% as compared to the average bariatric surgery program with a self-pay rate of only 3%:

Patient Benefits:

- Freedom of choice for surgeon & hospital

- No need to go through insurance pre-authorization requirements unless mandated by surgeon

- Viable option for those that don't have insurance coverage for weight loss surgery

- Able to be scheduled for surgery faster
- No last minute surgery cancellations due to insurance denial or additional requirements

Practice/Hospital Benefits:

- Higher profit margin
- No time required for staff to obtain insurance authorization
- Ease of determining surgery date – easier to schedule sooner
- Self-pay patients are often more motivated to succeed long-term and thus, more compliant since they have some 'skin in the game'. This enhances enjoyment of patient care and improves patient outcomes

Patient Risks:

- Risk of complications which may not be covered by their primary insurance.[11]
- Higher out of pocket expense

Practice/Hospital Risks:

- Risk of expediting or excluding helpful pre-operative testing/clearances
- Patients may rush into a decision that generally requires much contemplation so they are not as ready as possible for the changes that come along with bariatric surgery

The benefits tend to outweigh the risks. Thus, having a self-pay option for your bariatric surgery patients can be very helpful.

However, if you choose to add a self-pay program to your offering, you need to know that it can be difficult to find patients interested in self-pay. The most successful practices are those that are able to focus on creating a program that includes what these patients desire most. Experience shows this clientele completes very thorough research and desire the following:

* Experienced surgeon with a history of excellent outcomes and positive reviews

* Cost effective package price

* Personalized, professional and friendly service in a warm environment

* Concierge style care with seamless care delivery

* Clear communication

* Ongoing comprehensive support that is convenient and proven effective

Thus, when creating your self-pay program, care to address each of these elements is critical. The next step is to utilize marketing strategies that engage patients. Often non-traditional marketing measures work best such as online efforts along with some traditional marketing to pique interest. The traditional marketing helps those that are candidates for surgery without coverage realize that weight loss surgery is still a viable option for them. Once that happens, they tend to do most of their research online. This is where a strong online presence/ubiquity footprint helps them find you. You need to build a relationship with them so they choose to invest in themselves through you. This is conveyed online as well as from the first phone call or interaction with your office staff. It is absolutely critical that each step is addressed and monitored closely for process improvement opportunities.

**Trend #4: Need for Additional Revenue Streams**

It is no surprise that with dwindling government and private insurance payments, bariatric surgery practices/programs need to diversify and create additional revenue streams that complement bariatric surgery. This may feel adverse to some but such revenue streams actually complement the surgery and have been shown to improve patient outcomes. The most effective and appropriate options for consideration at this time include:

1. Retail

2. Medical Weight Loss

3. Pre/Post-Operative Comprehensive 12 Month Educational Weight Loss Program

4. Fitness

5. Back on Track services for long term patients who may be struggling

If you haven't added any of these additional products/services to your program, you will find that patients not only desire such services but they are beginning to expect them. In addition, with proper guidance and planning, they are easier to add than you may think.

## Trend #5: Increase in Patient/Family Expectations

Let's face it, in any service profession, the customer experience is what can make or break your reputation and business. In fact, this is a big reason why the healthcare industry is focusing on the customer experience in order to meet evolving industry and consumer demands.[12]

For any bariatric surgery program to attain a desirable market share, efforts need to be focused on three primary areas patients not only want but expect:

1. **Demand for Excellence:** Patients have a choice. They can search "Dr. Google" for anything they want to research and that includes options for weight loss surgery, your program, your reputation and your outcomes. They pay attention to top reviews, testimonials and are swayed by what they read or hear whether it is valid or not. Thus, you need to pay attention to every aspect (online and offline) that influences these sources. You need to provide service that is second to none (while also guiding appropriate care for each patient). It can be a tough spot because sometimes what the patient wants is not necessarily what they need. You can guide some of this by managing expectations and educating patients at every turn. Doing so online with creative content that speaks directly to them is a great way to show up during their search and also help them understand your philosophy and how you can best help them.

2. **Development of Comprehensive Centers:** Patients/ customers like convenience. This is the same for morbidly obese patients. It takes a great deal of courage for them to reach out for help so making their experience convenient

helps with your relationship and ultimately compliance. Back in 2010 (before it was the cool thing to do), we created a 10,000 square foot facility that includes medical weight loss, surgical weight loss, full fitness center, educational classroom and a retail store. We have never looked back. Our patients LOVE it and so do we. This model has been duplicated successfully and is well received. However, a comprehensive center isn't all you need. It really is just a building. You need the compassionate staff that brings the 'magic' to your space. In the end, it is your skill, education and relationship with your patients that results in above average outcomes and off the charts patient satisfaction.

3. **Desire for Concierge Care:** Concierge medicine is defined in Wikipedia as "a relationship between a patient and a primary care physician in which the patient pays an annual fee or retainer. This may or may not be in addition to other charges."[13] However, it is so much more than that! It is your relationship with your patient and your intent/desire to streamline their care so it is efficient, convenient and personalized. This doesn't mean let them run all over you and make unrealistic demands. In fact, that rarely happens as long as expectations are managed up front and communication is clear each step of the way.

These expectations are becoming more of the norm. When you think about it, isn't that what you would desire for your bariatric surgery experience? You may think such desires are more like unnecessary demands. However, when proper systems are put in place for customer service, phone etiquette, online presence, testimonial gathering, care pathways, patient communication and the like, it becomes easier to manage and more enjoyable for all.

**Trend #6: Increasingly Difficult Long Term Patient Follow-Up**

Keeping up with data requirements for your office and national bariatric databases as required by your Bariatric Surgery Center of Excellence designation can be overwhelming. This overwhelm is eased if you have proper systems in place...and staff who like to be your 'numbers person'. Nonetheless, long term follow-up is becoming increasingly difficult for a number of good reasons. The primary reasons include:

1. **Higher Co-Pays/Deductibles:** As we discussed previously, co-pays and deductible limits are rising with each passing year. As an employer, you know that healthcare costs are one of the primary expenses you have unless you are a smaller business and no longer offer them anymore due to the astronomical cost. Your patients feel this pain as well and tend to avoid appointments they feel they can miss. You know how it is after weight loss surgery. Patients are losing weight and they feel great! So why go pay a $50 co-pay if they don't have to (even if they love you and coming to your office)? This makes data collection difficult at best. It is also a time drain for staff if they have to track them down to see how they are and obtain the necessary data points.

2. **Transient Population:** The world has gone mobile and that includes people. It is extremely apparent in areas such as ours where there is a strong military population (thank you

for your service!) as well as just about any other place in the United States. If you have a travel surgery program, this makes it even more challenging to follow-up properly.

3. **Patient Independence/Potential for Poorer Outcomes:** When patients feel well, they become quite independent. This is a good thing – they all lose weight the first year. However, what happens if they didn't stay in touch for all of your education and didn't actually change underlying habits? If they begin to regain weight and have been independent, they often don't follow up because they are embarrassed or they may start to look for other diet miracles to help them at that point. This can adversely affect their outcomes and yours. Your ongoing relationship is what can prevent this from happening along with accountability, patient motivation and education as to what to expect each step of the way.

All of these issues make the need for creative ongoing patient support that is engaging and mobile necessary. Luckily the resources for online support and app development have never been easier. In fact, we offer all of our education on site as well as via a private membership site. They can also interact with our surgeon each and every week via a live educational webinar where they can ask questions. If they can't make it, not to worry, they have access to it in their membership site by the next day. Recording has never been easier – all you need is a computer or your smartphone along with an app or some simple to use editing software. Best yet, you can use content you create such as the weekly podcasts we do and post them to your website and any of your social media sites. Then you can transcribe them into your blog, optimize them with keywords and a title people search for and before you know it, you are showing up easily in the search engines while educating your patients (and potential patients) with fresh content on a regular basis.

This may sound a bit confusing but resources for creating attractive graphics/content are easy to obtain. It can also be quite a bit of fun – especially when you have a plan in place for making it all happen within a predictable system. More on this in Chapter 11.

**Trend #7: Increased Program Competition/Survival of the Fittest**

Remember I mentioned earlier that new Bariatric Surgery Programs are popping up across the United States? Well that is true and it is great for the other 99% of the obese population that aren't receiving services. It also creates competition. This is especially true for areas with a higher concentration of bariatric surgeons and bariatric programs. Yes, competition can be good! This is especially true if you have an abundance mindset. Competition tends to raise standards and improve access to care. However, it also creates the need for differentiation and can create significant financial stress.

If you've been around in this field for over 23 years as we have been, you know what I am talking about. You used to be the only surgeon in town (and might still have been independent) and your surgical schedule was booked out for 3+ months. You had a waiting list and were diligently trying to coordinate support services for your patients as best as you could.

Luckily, for us, we took a gamble on what the future held and decided to specialize solely in bariatrics and create a center that brought all of the necessary support services under one roof. Don't get me wrong, there have been tough times (especially since the practice is still independently owned/operated), but it has given us the opportunity to be different and to serve our patients in a personalized way. It has given us the chance to focus on the patient and their needs and create an environment that is appreciated by staff and patients alike. And now we have the pleasure of helping others do the same!

If you are feeling the pressure of competition, here are some key areas that can help you maintain or attain your edge for long term success:

- **Create Your Niche:** What is it that makes you different? What have you noticed your patients need that isn't currently being provided in your area? Is there a particular procedure you enjoy doing the most (primary procedures/ revisions/other)? What is your 'claim to fame' (most experienced/research driven/one stop shop/fitness/ outstanding customer service/convenience/cutting edge/ concierge care etc.)? Think about not only what your niche is but what your patients want/need. When you create your marketing plan, you will want to focus on their primary pain points (more on this later) along with your niche. Focus on their desired outcome, not just your assets.

- **Marketing Creativity (it's noisy out there):** You have likely noticed that the traditional marketing methods aren't enough…and they are really expensive. You will serve yourself well (and out shine your competition) if you integrate non-traditional (less expensive) marketing methods such as social media, videos, webinars and infographics. Being unique helps you differentiate your program as well. In addition, such methods help your ideal customers get to know you better and are the beginning of your relationship. These methods also keeps them coming back as your relationship matures.

- **Center of Excellence:** If you aren't already a designated Bariatric Surgery Center of Excellence then begin your plans to become designated. It's a good idea for many reasons such as ensured compliance with standards of care; prestige; marketing advantage; data management; insurance requirement for some companies among others.

- **Referral Program:** If you don't have a referral program then put one in place! Seriously, when you create raving fans of successful patients, they become your best advocates. And these are often the best referrals you can get! So why not reward them? It doesn't have to be anything big and often they want nothing at all. We will get into this later in the training with specific examples.

- **Physician Burnout Potential:** With competition, financial struggles, potential patient complications and/or staffing issues (among other things) comes stress. With stress comes burnout. As with any profession, physician burnout is real. Bariatric surgery is a high stress field. As you know, you are taking people who often have significant co-morbidity and electively operating on them. Fortunately, bariatric surgery is considered a safe procedure but you are still operating on patients who are compromised in many ways and may have habits that if not changed, can cause major complications (i.e. overeating or self-advancing their diet before instructed after surgery). It is important to remain cognizant of this potential and ensure that there is adequate coverage for time off. Also, practicing what you preach and exercising on a regular basis helps as well!

There will always be competition. It's important to have an abundance mindset and embrace the challenge in a positive and unique way. There are plenty of patients that need your help. It is helpful to understand your ideal patient, what they need, how you can best serve them and then market uniquely so you attract them to your program. Once they experience what you have to offer, help them share their story and experience with others. This will serve you well and bring more enjoyment.

## Chapter 2:

# Metrics that Make or Break a Bariatric Surgery Program

**"Risk comes from not knowing what you are doing."**

Warren Buffet

**Karol's *Must Know* Numbers**

Whether you enjoy numbers or not, you need to not only track them on a regular basis, you need to interpret them. Interpretation allows you to predict trends, set and measure goals, identify problems, budget properly and create/modify your plans for continued growth and financial stability.

After 20+ years managing physician practices and most of those years managing a bariatric surgery practice, I have key metrics that I recommend following on a weekly, monthly, quarterly or yearly basis. These key metrics focus on three primary areas; financial, marketing and clinical.

You can have a reliable and trustworthy employee gather the data for you if you desire but then it is critical for the physician(s) and management team to review them together on a monthly basis. I also like sharing key metrics with all staff so they understand your goals and how they can assist in meeting/exceeding them.

*Whether you enjoy numbers or not, you need to not only track them on a regular basis, you need to interpret them.*

You have hopefully been able to hand select your team (more on this in Chapter 12). Your employees are often the best people to come up with ideas as to new products/services patients may need as well as identify what may be causing any underlying trends/ problems you identify. They need to feel included as a part of the team and if they have that connection, my experience is that they will rise to the occasion when a challenge presents itself. Communication and respect for their ideas (even if not implemented) will help keep them engaged and loyal. This will help keep the corporation moving forward and a happier place to work.

*Staff need to feel included as a part of the team and if they have that connection, my experience is that they will rise to the occasion when a challenge presents itself.*

**Financial Metrics:**

Although there are other things I recommend tracking, below are what I believe to be the most important financial numbers to follow. Some are tracked weekly and others monthly. You can utilize a simple Excel spreadsheet for the weekly numbers and then roll everything up into a yearly spreadsheet for easy month to month comparison and trend analysis. In addition, some can be tracked by cost center (i.e. surgical, medical, fitness, retail) as appropriate. This helps when measuring cost center goal attainment or cost center trends.

- **Total Charges:** The total insurance and cash pay charges for services (for each cost center). I recommend tracking this weekly.

- **Total Payments:** The total insurance and cash pay receipts for services (for each by cost center). I recommend tracking this weekly.

- **Total Expenses:** The total office expenses including payroll (for each cost center if you want to get more specific). I recommend tracking this weekly.

- **Charge Entry Turnaround Time:** The average time it takes charges to be entered from the date/time of service. You want to keep this timeframe as low as possible (<24 hours if possible). I recommend tracking this monthly.

- **Retail Revenue:** Total revenue for our retail store (includes onsite and online sales). I recommend tracking this weekly.

- **Retail COGS:** Total Cost of Goods Sold for our retail store. I recommend tracking this weekly.

- **Retail Discounts:** Your retail store is a great place to reward your patients. In fact, you can utilize simple systems that track each of their purchases. Whenever they purchase, they get rewards points/money to use toward future purchases. Your patients will LOVE this. You can also use this mechanism for other promotions. I recommend tracking this total discount dollar amount monthly.

- **Profit/Loss:** Total revenue minus COGS and Expenses (for each cost center if you want to get more specific). I recommend tracking this weekly.

- **Adjusted FFS Collection Rate:** This is your adjusted fee for service collection rate. It is essentially your total charges minus any contractual write-offs. Over time, your desire is to collect 95% of the adjusted rate. I recommend tracking this monthly.

- **Aging Accounts Receivable (A/R):** This shows how fast you are getting paid and measured in various aging 'buckets'. These include <31 days, 31-60 days, 61-90 days, 91-120 days and >120 days. You will want to track this as a total and then divide it between insurance and patient responsibility. Your preference is to keep as much of your money to collect below 61 days if possible. This helps your staff track claims that aren't paid and work those accounts with the insurance company. The patient A/R is utilized to reach out to those with outstanding balances who are not making payments in an attempt to obtain payment and begin a collection procedure as appropriate. I recommend tracking this monthly.

- **Payer Mix/Average Reimbursement:** You will want to know what insurances you are billing and the average reimbursement for each by CPT code. This will help you know the amount that companies are paying on average. This data can be used for contract negotiation purposes. Also, you can drill down to which patients have the best paying insurances, where they work (if it is an employer policy) and develop a marketing plan specific to that entity/persons. I recommend tracking this monthly.

- **Payment at Time of Service:** This measures whether or not your employees at check-in/check-out are collecting co-pays and past balances. This is critical to long term viability. Co-pays should be expected at the time of service and if the patient can't pay any previous balances, then a payment plan should be put into place. I recommend tracking this monthly.

- **Overdue Accounts:** You need to be looking at overdue accounts, having staff call them for payment and determine when it is time for them to be sent to collections. I recommend tracking this monthly.

In addition to financial metrics, you must be measuring your marketing metrics. If you are a hospital based program, your relationship with your marketing department is critical. Together, track these numbers so you can make marketing modifications as necessary.

**Marketing Metrics:**

Below are some critical marketing metrics:

- **Seminar No Show Rate:** Track how many people were scheduled for your weight loss surgery seminar(s) and then how many actually showed. # No Show's/# Scheduled x 100 = No Show Percentage. I recommend tracking this monthly.

- **Seminar to Surgery Conversion Rate:** Track those people that attended a seminar and then how many actually had surgery. There is obviously a lag time for this so it has to be measured over a 6 month period. I recommend tracking this monthly.

- **Webinar to Surgery Conversion Rate:** The number of people coming in for a one on one physician consultation who viewed an online webinar (instead of coming in for a seminar) is ever increasing. I recommend requiring that they sign a document indicating they watched the webinar in its entirety prior to seeing the physician. Coincidentally, at the practices I work with, their webinar rate of conversion is often higher than their on-site seminar and generates a higher percentage of self-pay patients. It is exciting to help bariatric surgeons implement this in their office for a noticeable increase in total cases. I recommend tracking this monthly.

- **Marketing Campaign ROI:** No matter what marketing campaign you are running, you need to measure its return on investment (ROI). At least a 3:1 return is desirable. I recommend tracking it based upon actual surgeries (not just leads). This is more stringent but a better measure in my opinion. For example, if you run a Facebook ad, measure how many leads it brought in that month but also track the number of surgeries that result. If you spent $500 this month for a Facebook advertisement you are running (we usually create/ manage all of our ads/campaigns in house so there is no additional 3rd party fees), you want to show that you made at least $1,500 (easily covered by one insurance surgery) but if you end up with a self-pay surgery, your ROI goes up often to nearly 10:1. And if so, you should run the ad again based upon this data. I recommend tracking this monthly.

- **Referral Sources:** You MUST know where your referrals are coming from so you will know where to focus your efforts. It can get tricky though because if you are not getting referrals from a particular source (i.e. billboard) is it because that's not where your ideal patients look for information or is the billboard just in a poor location. If your referrals are coming in from a particular area (i.e. patients or physicians), you want that to continue or increase so you will want to nurture those relationships. I recommend tracking this monthly.

- **Zip Code Analysis:** In order to know what segment of the population you are penetrating, you need to do a zip code analysis. This simply means that you need to look at where most of your clients come from so you can determine where else you need to increase your efforts. I recommend tracking this monthly.

- **Patient Satisfaction:** You can measure this with standard post-visit patient satisfaction surveys. You will also have a gauge of this based upon any patient complaints you receive which need to be followed up on immediately. In fact, I recommend that every staff member have the ability and obligation to try to resolve any misunderstandings immediately. Fortunately, for most practices they are pretty rare. If you have a retail store, I recommend staff have the ability to provide discounts in the retail store as appropriate.

- **Total Surgeries Performed:** I like to track weekly the number of surgeries performed as well as what is scheduled. This allows program leaders/staff to proactively address any ramifications from a surgeon on vacation or discuss topics such as ways to streamline the seminar to surgery insurance authorization process.

Finally, what are most important are your patient outcomes. At the centers I consult with, I recommend developing pre and post-operative educational programs and services that help the patients understand how to keep their weight off for life. It is helpful to compare your metrics to the national benchmark within the MBSAQIP database if you are a Center of Excellence with the American College of Surgeons. Here are the main clinical metrics I recommend following on a monthly or quarterly basis:

**Clinical Metrics (measured quarterly):**

- **Overall Weight Loss (6 month, 1 year, 2 years):** I recommend measuring how much weight was lost by your patients particularly at 6 months, 1 year and 2 years after surgery.

- **Readmission Rate:** This measures if any of your patients were readmitted within 30 days of surgery. I also recommend tracking the reason for the readmission. This can lend itself to potential quality improvement activities.

- **Reoperation Rate:** This measures if any of your patients required an additional operation within 30 days of surgery.

- **Reduction of Comorbidities at 1 year:** I recommend tracking the overall reduction of co-morbidity percentage at 1 year after surgery. This should easily be obtained from the database associated with your Bariatric Surgery Center of Excellence.

- **Mean Operative Time:** This is the average time for each surgeon in the operating room from incision to close.

- **Average LOS:** This is the average length of stay your patients experience in the hospital

Numbers are important. These are the primary ones I recommend tracking regularly as indicated. Once you set up a system (if you haven't already) for collection of data, it becomes second nature. Setting up effective systems is the solution to most inefficiencies and frustrations in the work place.

## Chapter 3:

# Evolution of the 5 Profit Engines

Profitability is something you may not choose to openly discuss (although you likely desire it very much). It is true that you went into healthcare so you can help others. I did too and in fact, I am the last one you want checking patients in or discussing their bill. As a clinician, I chat with them too much, spend a lot of time teaching and want to do it all for free because I want to be helpful. Unfortunately, that is not the best plan of action. Especially in the field of bariatric surgery, patients cannot expect you to fix it all *for* them. You can give them the tools they need and teach them how to use these tools properly but they still need to do the work and have some skin in the game. I have been shown time and time again that people don't value "free". They just don't!

You also won't be able to help very many people if you can't cover your costs, attract an ideal team and grow your business. You will either go bankrupt or end up on the chopping block at the next hospital board meeting. Over the past couple of decades, my team and I have been perfecting various profit streams that will help you avoid this fate. Best yet, they are proven effective, make your job easier, keeps your patients and staff happier, increases your caseload with patients you enjoy the most and result in great patient outcomes.

***You won't be able to help very many people if you can't cover your costs, attract an ideal team and grow your business.***

The model I have created includes 5 Profit Engines and I am going to share them with you here and do a deep dive with specific actions on each engine shortly. I hope you are excited because these are not just ideas; they are well developed, tested and have been effective for many years at the Center for Weight Loss Success in Newport News, VA. Now they are being successfully implemented at other centers as well.

So, here they are:

---

### 5 Profit Engines of a 7-Figure Bariatric Program

1. Retail Profit Engine

2. Pre and Post-Surgical Program Profit Engine

3. Cash Pay Surgery Profit Engine

4. Incentivized Referral Program Profit Engine

5. Automated Marketing Program Profit Engine

---

And here is a little background regarding how these profit engines were developed.

If you would have told me 20 years ago that today my husband and I would own a 10,000 square foot state of the art facility and employ an awesome/loyal team that thrives helping others lose weight, get fit, surpass their health goals and enjoy the process along the way I would have said "No way!". You see, I was on my way to a career in hospital administration where I could make a difference in the lives of patients and care givers on a much bigger scale.

Somewhere along the way (i.e. after we began having children), I moved from the hospital setting to managing physician practices. I also began helping my bright and caring husband (who has always been ahead of his time), Dr. Thomas W. Clark build his dream practice which started as creating a bariatric surgery center. We are pretty cautious and conservative so we started small (which is always a good idea). Then it expanded to adding a medical weight loss practice that included fitness. Finally, the two businesses married up to form the first of its kind comprehensive weight loss center on the east coast called the Center for Weight Loss Success in Newport News, VA.

Our original tiny 7-11 building has turned into a brand new facility with every detail tended to by the two of us throughout construction with a builder that was fabulous. Complete with all of the worries that come along with it! I mean he is one of the lone independent bariatric surgeons in the state! As you likely know, it is *very difficult* to sustain an independent practice from a financial and managerial standpoint. You have no deep pockets and at the end of the day, you're responsible not only for patient care but the livelihood of a group of people you consider family. And my husband doesn't compromise the care of his patients. He is committed to extensive education and having all of the services they may need available to them to better ensure long-term weight loss success. Doing this is the right thing to do, but it is very expense. I am sure you can relate.

However, when you have a dream, you follow it and we are a team that supports each other through good times and bad and fortunately, there have been more good times than bad. This is because being an independent practice gives you the ability to do things the way you want to do them and allows you to keep your operations truly patient focused. Tom is actually the visionary and I am the creative, 'go to' gal. I am the one who builds the team and makes it happen. Of course, this is also so he can guide the clinical care and ensure patients are cared for properly. In fact, my team and I have set up systems so he can engage with patients each and every week in the form of podcasts, webinars, online contests and even fitness videos featuring him and our various personal trainers. It is actually a lot of fun (and has a side benefit of increasing our online organic traffic). More on this later.

As I mentioned earlier, I am the one in the office that likes to give everything away. However, when you own and operate a business, you have to balance quality with cost effectiveness and efficiency while maintaining profitability in order to survive and grow. Along the way, we were able to create a business that accommodates all of these aspects. It has given 'birth' to some key strategies that we have carefully developed to not only survive but thrive and have the ability to exceed patient expectations. I call these strategies the 5 Profit Engines of a Successful Bariatric Surgery Practice. Although this sounds entirely financial based, each actually contributes to improved patient outcomes, better patient engagement, growing the practice and having some fun along the way.

Now I use this formula to help other physicians and bariatric programs grow as well so they can reach more patients that need their services and experience consistent profitability. It is very rewarding to say the least! My goal here is to describe these engines in specific steps to help you understand how they work and how to implement them in your own program.

Before we get to the specifics, it is important to cover something I am asked about all the time. "What are the best marketing strategies working right now for getting more patients through the door?" So here is what I find to be *proven* strategies to do just that. Best yet, they cost less than traditional marketing methods. My staff and I will even teach a "Do It Yourself" Marketing Program for Bariatric Surgeons upon request. I love creating personalized success strategies with bariatric surgeons so if you want a free 30 minute strategy session, sign up at www.smarturl.it/bookkarol or e-mail me at Karol@WeightLossPracticeBuilder.com

## Chapter 4:

# Top Marketing Strategies for Attracting Your Ideal Patients

If you have found a marketing specialist that is getting you great results in terms of attracting your ideal patients with a positive ROI and meeting/exceeding your goals, then I applaud you! That is not easy to do and you should stick with them.

More likely, you are not fully satisfied with your bariatric surgery program marketing efforts and want more. However, as a clinician, this is not what you were trained to do and quite possibly something you dislike doing. Nor do you have the time! In fact, the words marketing and sales may have negative connotations for you because they are often related to scams and being taken advantage of which never feels good.

However, helping people improve their health and do the things that bring them the most enjoyment feels great! Seeing someone with tears in their eyes as they step on the scale and hit that 75 or

100 pound weight loss mark makes you smile yet tear up at the same time. Watching someone work out in your fitness center that could barely walk to their mailbox a few months ago makes you proud. You know what I mean because if you are reading this, you help people overcome obstacles and have these experiences each and every day. And it never gets old.

So how do you bring in more patients with integrity and without feeling 'salesy'? How do you get your desired marketing results without having to do all of the work?

Marketing begins with your brand and your brand is more than your logo and color scheme. Your brand is the *relationship* you have with your patients. You are an integral part of this relationship as well as each and every one of your employees. You know your patients the best. You know their fears, pains, desires, what they love and what they hate. This is critically important to your marketing efforts.

***Your brand is the relationship you have with your patients.***

You see, people make choices and purchases based upon feelings. The experience that they have with you and your program is what creates their feelings – and what they will remember (and share with others).

When you think about creating a positive experience that helps your patients alleviate their fears, do more of what they love and less of what they dislike, it feels good. And yet, it's still marketing and sales. You are selling the experience. You know it is good for them and that it will impact them positively for a long time to

45

come. That's the thing about bariatric surgery. It is a relationship and your patients don't forget you or what you/your staff have done for them. They are grateful forever.

*People make choices based upon feelings created by their experience with you and your program – this is what they will remember and share with others.*

Unfortunately, we had a hard time finding an effective marketing company and were tired of spending a lot of money with little or no return. We abide by the mantra you can do anything you set your mind to so we chose to learn (a lot) and create our own strategies to connect with our ideal patients. We actually operate our entire marketing program in house through our staff that knows our patients best. You might be surprised what hidden talents your staff has if you ask and give them the chance to grow. This has proven to be wildly successful and much less costly for us.

When you say "experienced" it generally means that you have learned lessons the hard way in a particular field. You have gone out on a limb, advanced your knowledge with some successes and a lot of failures.

Well, I feel confident in saying that we are very experienced! So it's time to share with you not only what works, but works very well when it comes to effectively marketing your bariatric surgery program. This means attracting your ideal patients, creating positive relationships, growing your program and having fun along the way.

I could spend a lot of time on marketing fundamentals but I know what you are most interested in are the steps that will get you to faster success along with specific tactics you can implement right away.

*You might be surprised what hidden talents your staff has if you ask and give them the chance to grow.*

Thus, after a lot of study and years of practical application, I am going to share with you a simple big picture and then 6 steps that will serve as a laser focused guide for you and your team. As a big picture in the lifecycle of getting more patients, *you want 4 things to happen.* They include:

1. Attract your ideal customers/patients

2. Build a quality relationship with them

3. Convert them to a weight loss surgery procedure or other services as appropriate

4. Turn these patients into Raving Fans that send more patients your way (and promote you to their PCP)

In order to make these 4 things happen, you will want to follow something called a GREAT process for marketing success. I tried to make it only 3 steps but in reality, it is 6 important steps. As a warning, most people like to start at Step 5 since when you are fulfilling tactics, you are *doing* something. However, the reality is that Step 5 will be somewhat worthless (or random) and can cause you to waste a fair amount of money if performed prior to completing Steps 1-4. You see planning (even if you think it is boring) will save you immense amounts of time and frustration. Like most of you, I like an adventure that doesn't include a map but not when I need to be efficient and I am determined to obtain a

47

specific result. Just trust me; you need to do these in order. And I also included a case study at the end so you can see the plan in action.

---

**Karol's GREAT Process for Bariatric Surgery Program Marketing Success**

1. **Goal** : Determine Your Goal/Desired Outcome

2. **Rare:** Verify What Makes You a Rare Gem/Unique

3. **Emotional Triggers:** Identify the Primary Pain Points of Your Ideal Patient/Client (your Avatar)

4. **Approach:** Map out Your Strategy (Right Market/Right Message/Right Media)

5. **Tactics:** Create Your Actionable Calendar & Implement Appropriate Tactics (most people mistakenly start here)

6. **Test:** Measure, Refine, Re-Deploy

---

**Step 1: Goal: Determine Your Goal/Desired Outcome:**

So what is it you want to accomplish? And don't think too small. Where do you want to grow? Do you want more cases? Do you want more retail revenue? Do you want to implement a new patient educational program? Do you want to increase the number of people at your seminars? What is it? The key here is to keep it simple and make it measurable.

Depending upon the size of your organization and your team, you may have more than one goal. But I caution you to keep it simple and work towards some great wins before you get too greedy with the process.

Have you heard of the *12 Week Year*?[14] It's a book well worth reading and a system that improves your ability to get things done. The underlying premise is that the one thing holding you back from achieving more in your life is execution. You don't do the work necessary to make your goals happen. In the 12 Week Year, instead of thinking of your goals in terms of 12 months, you fulfill your goals in 12 weeks and move on to the next. One of the great things about that with regards to your marketing plan is that it keeps you moving, keeps you accountable (you only have 12 weeks right?) and if your marketing strategy was an online evergreen one (almost like being on auto pilot), you are on to your next strategy while your previous one is still working for you! It's wonderful.

Bottom line for this step is to identify your desired outcome. When you do, be sure that it is simple and measurable.

**Step 2: Rare: Verify What Makes You a Rare Gem/Unique**

When I say "you", of course I mean what makes you and your program stand out in a crowd? What would make a person choose you over other bariatric surgeons? It's a question you might not think about often. I mean it's considered arrogant to tout your talents around town isn't it? However, when you have a crowded market and competitors across the street or across town, you need to figure out what makes you unique. Why do your patients choose you and your program?

You need to know this because you will use it as a way to attract patients. You will understand this better as we dig deeper into these steps. In fact, if you used it as a message such as "Come to Program X because we are the best." that wouldn't work. It could be viewed as arrogant and annoying. People want to know *why* you are the best.

A better way to use your strengths is as a complement to the problems and fears that your potential patients may have. For example, if they are fearful of surgery, knowing you have the most experienced surgeons would be helpful. Or if your potential patients live in a remote part of your state and will be far from home, it would be comforting for them to know that you have a seamless travel surgery program so that they and their family will have their needs met in a convenient and comfortable way. Knowing your unique competitive advantage is important and will be paired with what you identify in Step 3. This is very different from just saying we are the best or we are the most experienced without linking it to why that would be important to the patient and what 'pain' you are able to solve for them.

**Step 3: Emotional Triggers: Identify the Primary Pain Points of Your ideal Patient (Your Avatar)**

Now you and your team need to brainstorm your ideal customer or avatar. And it shouldn't be 'everyone'. Think about them and define the following (be specific). As you do this, put in your mind a picture of a patient you really, really enjoy working with. Define these aspects as if you are describing them and then broaden it some as desired.

- Age range

* Gender

* Occupation

* Income Level

* Educational Level

* Geographic Location

* Co-morbidities

* PCP

* Insurance Type

Once you have defined your ideal patient, think about what their main problems, challenges and pain points (what's really bothering them that caused them to come see you for treatment). You will want to know that because in your marketing message, you are going to want to agitate that problem just a bit so that you can adequately catch their attention. This may seem silly to you but it is very important to be very specific. You are going to create your marketing message as if you are speaking *directly* to that patient you were thinking of that you enjoy working with.

Once you come up with a long list, separate out what you feel are the top 5 pain points. These will be helpful as you develop your content and marketing plan.

### Step 4: Approach: Map Out Your Strategy (Right Market/ Right Message/Right Media)

This sounds involved but it is fairly straight forward. This is where you will create your strategy for reaching the ideal client you identified above. This is your *right market*. If you know your outcome/goal and who it is that you are trying to reach, that's half the battle.

After that, it is time to determine the *right message*. For this, you will combine one of their top pain points to what it is that you are offering. In your message, you want to catch their attention in an authentic, sincere and ethical way. This is the time to get your team together and brainstorm. If you are promoting weight loss surgery and one of your staff has had the procedure, they would be a great reality check as to whether or not your message resonates.

For clinicians, the marketing message is what may feel uncomfortable. However, if you tie it to an educational blog or video (something you talk about or teach every day), it makes more sense and is perceived as more valuable to the patient. You can see a great example of this in the case study presented shortly.

If you follow this method, then what you are actually creating is something called a "lead magnet" which is something that is perceived to be valuable to your ideal customer (and great information they need). It is something that they are willing to exchange their name and e-mail or other contact information in order to obtain it. Once you have that, you can continue to nurture your relationship with additional helpful information and at some point, if they make the decision to pursue treatment, you will likely be the one they will choose. You will be top of mind.

Finally, you must determine the *right media*. You can choose one type of media or test your message through a number of media sources. Some choices are listed below. The more you test your media channels, the more you will understand which are your most successful and which you can avoid at this time.

Your media choice will be dependent upon where your ideal patient 'hangs out'. Depending upon the demographic you identified, they could get their information through traditional marketing (i.e. brochures, direct sales, TV, radio, printed advertisements, and direct mail). Another type of marketing source is on the internet (i.e. e-mail campaign, social media, blogs, podcasts and resulting search engine optimization). For healthcare, another source is direct referral from their primary care provider or some other healthcare professional. In this case, you actually market to the healthcare provider directly. They are usually interested in your outcome data and ease of referral to your center. In addition, they desire a positive patient experience and communication regarding the patient. Nurturing these relationships tends to be very time consuming and somewhat frustrating because you have to get by the 'gatekeeper' at the front desk. Nonetheless, these efforts can be very worthwhile.

**Step 5: Tactics: Create Your Actionable Calendar & Implement Appropriate Tactics (most people mistakenly start here)**

Here is where people get excited. You have your ideal patient identified, you know where they hang out, and you have created your message that identifies their pain point and why your service or product is their solution. Now it is time to create your actionable calendar. This identifies specific plans for creating your marketing ad, details about printing or online ad approval/placement, who has responsibility for each action, what is being posted where and when (day/time). It is all in front of you so you and your team are crystal clear as to when the campaign is going to run, what the budget is and how to measure the outcome. Now is the time to clarify questions and then deploy the plan.

Here are a few tips for the Tactic step in the GREAT process:

- Start Small (it can be very time consuming)

- Consider Your Internal vs. External Resources/Assets so you might not have to start from scratch

- Set Up Your Schedule and Stick to It

- Automate Posts When Possible (saves time & energy)

- Don't Schedule Too Far In Advance – Trends Change

- Be Ready to Respond to a Trend in Your Area of Expertise

- Use Graphics/Video (be wary of copyright laws and have signed release from clients on file)

- Each Post Should Have a Clear Call to Action (CTA) so the patient knows exactly what to do or where to call

**Step 6: Test: Measure, Refine, Re-Deploy**

Keeping track of your analytics can help determine if you are spending your time and efforts in the right way. From a financial perspective, your return on investment (ROI) should be at least a 3:1 ratio (if $500 was spent your return should be $1,500 or more). You can track your analytics in a variety of ways:

- Google Analytics

- Facebook Analytics

- Internal statistics

- Other lead generation software if you use them for lead capture such as Leadpages or Clickfunnels

Once you determine your ROI, it is time to determine if you just need to tweak your ad, do some split testing or re-deploy an entirely different ad. Usually it is a matter of tweaking your ad message, where your message is being deployed or the specific market where you chose to send it. Thus, you want to look at your market, message and media source(s) and make changes as necessary.

# Case Study: Bariatric Surgery Program

**Step 1: Goal: Increase number of cases/month/surgeon to 24**

**Step 2: Rare/Unique Characteristics**

- Most experienced surgeons in the region

- Good Reputation

- Best-Selling Author

**Step 3: Emotional Triggers**

- Fear of surgery

- Poor health/co-morbidities

- Not feeling 'normal' and fitting in/being able to do everyday activities

- Joint pain

- Lack of energy

**Step 4: Approach**

- Right market: men/women who need to lose 75+ pounds, are interested in surgery but have a lot of questions, educated, professional, committed to change

- Right message: Is weight loss surgery right for you? Get your free book from best-selling author and the regions most experienced weight loss surgeon. Sign up here or call (999) 999-9999

- Right media: Facebook ad for people who met the demographic above and lived in the same state as the program

**Step 5: Tactics**

- The ad was created and deployed as a Facebook campaign for the identified audience. Re-targeting pixels were set in place and an ad buy for a maximum spend of $25/day for 30 days was put into place.

**Step 6: Test**

- Measure/Refine/Re-Deploy: It took 3 tries to get the ad approved on Facebook which is common with nearly all weight loss ads. Once approved, the ad spend the first month was $540. The campaign resulted in 30 books being requested/downloaded. All were put into an e-mail sequence. 4 people have contacted the office and scheduled 1:1 visits with the physician. Two are insurance and two are potential self-pay surgeries. One self-pay followed through thus far with surgery resulting in a 9:1 ROI

- While the ROI is great, this is not meeting the initial objective. Thus, we will refine the ad with split testing 2 different ad messages and review our follow-through for interested patients

- In the meantime, with the great 9:1 ROI, the current ad will continue!

*To be a sustainable business, you must be able to create messages that matches the wants/needs of your ideal client.*

As a summary, the marketing tactics we have mastered that are currently working for our practice and other practices we work with include:

- Platform/Brand/Relationships

- Online Webinars

- Organic Search (website, keywords, optimization)

- Targeted e-Mail Marketing (sales & educational)

- Text Messaging

- Physician Referrals

- Testimonials (written/video)

- Engaging Social Media Posts with Editorial Calendar for ease of implementation – Facebook, Pinterest, You Tube, Twitter

- Best-Selling Author/Books

- Facebook Campaigns/Lead Magnets/Sales Funnel

- Facebook Live

- Onsite Electronic Sign

- Optimized Rich Content (video, audio, written)

- Building Our Ubiquity Footprint Over Time

- Weight Management University for Weight Loss Surgery™ turnkey educational program

- Clear Branding

- Other Helpful Options:

  o Radio/Expert Presentations/Interviews

  o Medical Tourism

  o Podcasts

  o Fliers

  o Referral Program

  o Cross-Selling

  o Posters

  o Radio/TV Personality Having Surgery

  o Donations

  o Letting local organizations utilize our space (foot traffic)

You don't need to introduce all of these tactics to your plan. You just need to implement the ones that interest you the most and that you feel will get the right message, to the right market (people) via the right media option. In fact, if you try to do too many tactics at once, you will feel frustrated, overwhelmed and financially drained (and drive your team crazy).

If you feel as if you need assistance selecting the tactic(s) that are right for you or assistance implementing your chosen tactics, there are resources available. If you desire a free strategy session, feel free to reach schedule one at www.smarturl.it/bookkarol or e-mail me at Karol@WeightLossPracticeBuilder.com

As for the tactics that are not producing a positive ROI for us at this time, they include:

- Traditional Marketing (TV, Radio, Print)

- Mobile Applications – We have used private apps in the past but discovered there are so many weight loss apps out there that utilization didn't warrant the financial outlay at this time.

Now it's time to address each profit engine in greater detail.

## Chapter 5:

# Profit Engine #1 – Retail Profit Engine

The Retail Profit Engine is one of the most powerful of the 5 profit engines for creating a successful bariatric program. This profit engine has been proven to add up to $40,000.00 of additional recurring revenue each month for programs with a single surgeon. Yes, that's up to $480,000 of additional revenue annually with a single surgeon program. This revenue will be higher with each additional surgeon. Quite frankly, having this additional cost center cushions inconsistencies with your operating revenue and supplements your income either way (while helping your patients succeed). It is also a great way to *profit share* between surgeons and the hospital for hospital based programs as well.

I hate to be blunt, but if you are one of those people who say "Retail isn't for me or my patients", you need to get over it! Seriously! If your patients aren't buying quality protein products and vitamins from you, then they are buying sub-standard products from somewhere else. You owe it to yourself and to your patients to offer retail nutritional and vitamin products.

However, I want to make a distinction for you. You need to be providing them with physician prescribed protein products and pharmaceutical grade vitamins. You will be most successful if you sell items that they cannot obtain at local stores. Why? Because they are of a higher quality and you will be providing them with something unique. You cannot compete with the large vitamin store prices. They will always out price you (or else you will sell at a loss) because you cannot compete with their volume ordering which results in their lower wholesale cost and lower prices. What we have found is that the physician prescribed products also tend to taste better (if you do your homework) which puts you at an advantage over larger chain stores.

*If your patients aren't buying quality protein products and vitamins from you, then they are buying sub-standard products from somewhere else.*

I can confidently say we can help just about any practice/health system set up a retail store and turn a profit almost immediately. We help them keep their store profitable while growing it over time with monthly specials and marketing materials. This comes from experience selling the best quality, best tasting products and promoting them in a way that keeps patients happily coming back for more.

As a side note, a robust store generally does not occur by selecting one company that has protein products and signing a contract with them so you can only offer their products. It's not impossible, but more challenging. Patients want and need more variety. In addition, some vendors have great tasting protein shakes and yet their protein bars have either too many carbohydrates or taste terrible. Other vendors may have wonderful snacks but nasty tasting protein shakes or soups. You need to taste test before you decide to sell the product.

If you are hesitant, let me take the pressure off. The joy in selling nutraceuticals in your office is that you (the physician) are NOT the salesperson. In fact, you are likely already prescribing a certain amount of protein to your post-operative patient along with certain vitamins. All you are doing with a retail store is making it convenient for patients to purchase those on the spot without YOU completing the sale. Even better, if done properly, it keeps them coming back and bringing their family and friends! This is a win-win for everyone.

*The joy in selling nutraceuticals in your office is that you (the physician) are NOT the salesperson.*

Here's your step-by-step plan to build or enhance your retail store:

1. **Create your plan/budget for success:** Having an implementation plan and realistic budget with agreed upon minimal, target and stretch goals sets the stage for swift implementation. It also provides for an immediate return on investment (ROI) and lack of wasted time, resources and energy. Your goals will be dependent upon the size of your store and the number of your surgeons.

   You will also need to determine whether or not you are going to create an e-store for a greater reach and ease of ordering. A number of sales systems can accommodate both on-site and e-commerce as well. It is desirable to keep on-site and e-commerce sales in one system so that inventory can be maintained more efficiently. It is best to keep it simple at the beginning with just an on-site store but I mention e-commerce so that you can proactively ensure that it is a part of your software selection if e-commerce is included in your long-term plan.

Numbers are important. You should know what products have the highest sales, who your top buyers are (so you can reward them) and what products have the highest profit margin. It also helps to package some of your products together (i.e. vitamin pack) for higher sales and to offer a tempting discount for your patients.

Within your sales software, you will want to categorize each item you sell. I recommend leaving like items grouped together on your budget. However, you will still be able to drill down for each item within your sales software. For example, on your budget you might just have vitamins and nutritional products but in your sales system, you can actually look at each category such as shakes, bars, soups, snacks, entrees, and desserts. You can also look at sales by vendor. Your categories can grow as your store grows. It is important to note that if you plan to branch out into e-commerce, some software systems end up using these categories automatically to populate your online e-store. Thus, you will want to categorize them appropriately in a way customers would search for them online.

As for capital investment, you can begin by operating your store out of a closet. Thus, the only requirements would be sales software on one of your existing computers, a bar code reader (optional), shelving and your selected product. You can get my list of our favorite vendors at our website www.WeightLossPracticeBuilder.com/FreeResources. I place the resources online because they are updated frequently.

I recommend tracking your retail revenue/expenses as a separate cost center within your accounting software or this can be tracked as a totally separate business account depending upon ownership of the retail store and your preference. This is very important so you can track income, cost of goods sold, expenses and retail sales tax easily.

If you don't already have it, you will need to set up retail sales and use tax account with your state's government tax agency. Sales tax generally needs to be paid monthly and can usually be done easily online.

For some expenses that may be shared with your overhead office expenses, I recommend including them based upon the square footage of the store. For example, in one of our practices, the square footage is 10,000 feet and the store is 1,500 square feet. Thus, for telephone, rent and utilities, grounds maintenance and the like, they allocate 15% of the total monthly cost to the retail store. Salaries can be shared as well for this cost center depending upon the manpower needed for your particular size retail store.

Taking these things into consideration, a *basic* retail store budget outline might include:

**Revenue:**
- Vitamins
- Nutritional Products
- Other
- Shipping & Handling (for e-commerce only)

Total Revenue

**Cost of Goods Sold (COGS):**

- List each vendor you purchase products from to sell in your retail store

Total COGS

**Gross Profit:**

Total Revenue – COGS = Gross Profit

**Expenses:**

- Accounting
- Advertising & Promotion
- Bank Fees
- Credit Card Discount Fees
- CRM (Customer Relationship Marketing Software if you don't already have this in your current system)
- Event Supplies
- Grounds Maintenance
- Office Supplies
- Packaging Supplies
- Payroll
- Printing & Reproduction
- Rent
- Repairs & Maintenance
- Sales Operating Software
- Sales Tax Payable
- Shipping & Handling (for e-commerce)
- Telephone
- Uniforms (if applicable)
- Utilities

- Website

Total Expenses

**Net Income:**

Gross Profit – Expenses = Net Income

2. **Decide upon your timeframe for implementation:** Your retail store can be up and running in as little as 1 week depending upon how many products you desire to sell. If you are planning on a larger storefront, plan on 4-8 weeks. The timeframe is less as long as you follow a set plan as outlined here.

Many vendors will private label your products. This means that they will send them to you with your logo on them. This is great for brand recognition. However, this is not usually possible until a certain volume of consistent ordering is established. This volume is different for each vendor. You do not need to get worried about this at the beginning and some never choose not to private label at all.

As your store grows, I recommend private labeling as many items as you can as long as it won't result in too much product in your store that ends up as a loss when it becomes outdated and is disposed of instead of being sold. If you choose to private label, this will lengthen the timeframe for product delivery so you will need to take this into account as you determine the opening date for your retail store.

3. **Determine the right size store for your situation:** Your retail space can be as small as a closet or as large as our biggest storefront which is 1,500 square feet. In fact, you can begin operating from a closet and grow from there. This is also a

great way to 'test the waters'. If you are skeptical about having a retail store. Be careful though since skepticism by those in charge can prevent your store from ever getting off the ground. Trust me, you want a retail store. The benefits far outweigh any risks.

4. **Pick your products:** Product selection depends upon 4 things including: taste (for obvious reasons); nutritional content (that supports what your patients need); desire to private label (or not) and space (for storage requirements). Start small, see what sells best and then increase your par levels of stock.

A retail store may require a mindset change for you. For many clinicians (including myself), retail may feel "icky" or "salesy".

I can recommend tried and true vendors for you to evaluate at www.WeightLossPracticeBuilder.com/FreeResources. Then, I recommend you obtain samples and have you and your staff complete a taste test. Once you find quality products you really like, it becomes very easy to promote them to your patients.

You can also experiment with various ways to prepare your nutritional supplements. For example, nearly everyone on our staff drinks a protein shake for breakfast. The one we use is delicious and starts our day out with 29 grams of protein and just 15 grams of carbs (the great 2:1 ratio you are likely familiar with). Some like to add their coffee to their shake as part of the water, others like to add an extract for a varied flavor and others like to add peanut butter protein powder (like me).

I recommend you let your staff purchase your protein products at cost. You want them to be very familiar with the products. In this way, promotion to patients becomes second nature. They are excited as they talk to the patients and sales happen with much less effort.

5. **Set up your sales systems:** Efficiency requires systemization. It also requires a natural balance of systemization with high customer service. You see your sales system is a combination of technology and personalized service.

When selecting your sales system, you can either integrate the product sales in your current computer system or integrate easy low cost solutions that also provide for an e-store and rewards programs for your patients to enjoy. The former is helpful for smaller stores and the latter positions you better for rapid growth. Neither is right or wrong, it just goes back to your overall goal(s).

It is not mandatory, but rewards programs can be set up in a variety of ways and truly boost sales. You can do something as simple as 10% off for every $100 spent or get a bit more savvy with a program that tracks all sales and offers money back depending upon the amount spent (even online). Or, you can integrate both! The sky is the limit and is only constrained by your imagination (and the imaginations of your awesome staff).

The bottom line is to have a system that is reliable and easy to use. It is helpful if an e-mail system is included (which is usually the case) along with e-commerce as I mentioned earlier. Your system should also track inventory. I have used systems that are totally manual to systems that have every bell and whistle you want. Make sure that it will support your current needs without adding significantly to your overhead and are able to grow with you over time. If you want to learn about some of my system recommendations, visit www.WeightLossPracticeBuilder.com/FreeResources.

6. **Train your staff:** Not only is technology training necessary but having a "cheerleader" who enjoys sales is extremely helpful. Customer service training is a great way to not only help your store sales, but increase patient referrals and the overall positive attitude/atmosphere throughout all service points of your program.

If you are hiring someone new to run your store and be your sales associate, I recommend hiring someone with an interest in heath/wellness but not a clinician or typical medical professional. I recommend hiring someone who loves sales and events. If you can get someone who is talented at creating graphics and sales materials as well, then that's an added bonus you will appreciate more than you know.

One of my greatest aha moments was when I was able to stop micro managing the retail store and let someone who loves sales take over. Surrounding yourself with great staff who understands your vision, are loyal, self-directed, happy and creative will exponentially increase the speed of your business growth and goal attainment. Then your job is to challenge them with new goals and be sure to treat them well.

I have always believed that if I can hire someone with excellent communication and customer service, I can teach them the rest. The interesting thing I have found is that if they have excellent customer service, they are usually also eager to learn new things and to do things right. These individuals are like a sponge and respond well to a positive example and are able to learn things quickly (especially if your operating systems are well documented).

I like to hire committed, self-directed employees and then challenge them with an outcome…not a task. They will likely rise to the occasion and come up with something spectacular in half the amount of time you would. I have more recommendations for effective practice management in Chapter 12.

7. **Promote your products:** As I mentioned earlier, providing your staff (and yourself) with a cost effective way to use your retail products will help them promote them to others. It's easy to promote your products when they believe in them and use them personally.

You can easily integrate promotion and education regarding your vitamins and supplements at office visits, in educational materials, via e-mail, text and/or social media. Having a promotional plan makes this easier and predictable so you never miss a beat…or sale!

*It's easy to promote your products when you believe in them and use them personally.*

Once you get up and running, you will want to do a monthly calendar that outlines your specials, new products and monthly events. You can do as little or as much as you want. Your calendar helps guide your posts and e-mails to your patients. Texts as well if you desire.

For example, in one month you may want to promote your B-Complex vitamins. That month you write a blog about energy and the effect these vitamins has on energy and weight loss. You then do a quick video (even on Facebook live) and post your blog and your video at different times on each of your social media channels. Your e-mail to patients includes a link to the blog and the video as well as specifics about the vitamin special. If you have an e-store, you can link directly to the product. Often you can have the option within your e-store software for them to indicate if they want it shipped or if they want to pick it up at your store (to avoid shipping). You have to make it simple! Once you get this up and running, you will actually be making sales while you sleep.

There are many more tactics with regards to this intellectual material you create that can significantly increase your online presence. With proper use of key words, you will also increase your organic search engine optimization. It's amazing what can happen once you get some momentum. Another beautiful aspect is that this is essentially free other than the time and effort you/your staff spend setting everything up and creating content. Your costs can increase if you utilize an outside source but even so the cost should not be significant. Your resulting ROI should be positive with the additional sales coming in.

8. **Track your positive ROI:** As I mentioned before, I recommend you track your retail store as a separate cost center. In this way, it is easier to track revenue, cost of goods sold, sales tax and any other associated costs. We recommend doing this at least monthly and specific to any promotions you offer (monitor those sales spikes). This will help you fine tune your strategies for rapid growth and marketing with a positive ROI.

If you find you are not experiencing a positive ROI (which is extremely rare), watch out for these common culprits:

- Improper allocation of corporate overhead to this cost center inflating expenses (more common with hospital programs)
- Poor product selection
- Lack of enthusiastic sales associates/employees
- Too many free giveaways
- Lack of coordinated promotion and follow-up
- Products not properly displayed
- Poor buy in from staff/practitioners
- Poor understanding of proper Par levels resulting in over-ordering

The great thing is that all of these culprits can be corrected for better product management and higher sales. After a period of three months, you should be able to better predict appropriate par levels and have your systems in place for proper marketing and sales. If you have one month with a poor ROI, address it immediately because this is not the norm.

9. **Implement growth strategies:** Once you have your retail store up and running, monitor what is working well, what needs fine tuning and what needs to be eliminated. Brainstorm growth strategies with your front line employees and be open to new "out of the box" ideas that make sense with your plan (see step 1).

Your Retail Profit Engine can be one of your most fun endeavors. It is also something you can incorporate for maximum promotion through your events and support groups. Store discounts will also help incentivize all your other 4 bariatric program profit engines.

Coordinating necessary post-operative education with your products will help sales and organic search engine optimization. You can also use these products to launch a medical weight loss program and/or to assist your patients with weight loss prior to surgery. Another win-win for everyone since as you know, weight loss prior to surgery can make surgery a safer endeavor due to the liver shrinking effects and improved blood sugar control.

## Chapter 6:

# Profit Engine #2 – Pre and Post-Surgical Program Profit Engine

This profit engine focuses on how to improve patient engagement & outcomes with ease while adding another revenue stream to your program, even if you don't understand "tech" or don't have time to make it happen on your own.

The Pre & Post Surgery profit engine is not only an additional revenue stream but it takes all of the education you and your staff do every day and streamlines it into a more thorough, convenient and engaging way of delivery that has been shown to increase patient satisfaction and outcomes. And who doesn't want more of that?

Implementing this profit engine does not take your personal instruction away. Rather, it augments your instruction with easy to access cost effective written, video and audio resources. So no matter how your patient learns best, you have it covered. It also provides them with resource materials to review on their own and is shown to decrease the number of calls to your office.

As you know, an educated patient with clear expectations is a better prepared patient. This results in less confusion and potential misunderstandings and/or misinformation. This profit engine also provides additional resources for their significant other. I recommend including their significant other (or support person) be included every step of the way so they are informed and able to help avoid or assist with managing inevitable saboteur moments.

Perhaps you already have an educational program in place that includes a charge. This is appropriate because the services are necessary for ultimate success and something that is not covered by insurance. If you do, I commend your efforts and encourage you to make sure your education is also available in a convenient membership site for easy reference. If you do not have a robust educational program, then this is something I recommend you consider adding.

If you want to develop this profit engine for your practice, here are the steps to make that happen:

1. **Determine what your patient needs most:** Patients rarely think they need education…unless they don't have it. But you and your staff know better – especially when it comes to weight loss surgery.

   If you are repeating the same instructions over and over, then why not put it into a book (inexpensively published and printed through Amazon Create Space) or an online course within a private membership site? The online course can complement onsite instruction and be a great reference for your patients. It also sets you apart and is the beginning to a full program (if you don't have one already) that you can charge separately for prior to surgery. This online access allows you to keep the content fresh and add all of the resources you provide them with separately (i.e. recipes, shopping lists) in one convenient location. You can also track what your patients have accessed which is great for added accountability.

Some of our practices include other services as well such as personal training visits, fitness membership, nutritional counseling, retail products and the like. I find that is extremely helpful and give the patient something tangible which adds value to their purchase.

2. **Create interactive, engaging content to educate and support them (written, audio, video):** You probably already have a lot of these assets created. If not, don't worry, audio and video can easily be done yourself without a lot of 'tech'. Your smartphone and an app or software like Camtasia, iMovie or Final Cut for video does the trick and then within these programs you can separate the audio. Presto – you have audio for podcasts or for people to listen to on the go and video for those who learn visually in addition to any written materials.

Patients prefer that you be yourself so you don't have to stress that you have to be perfect. Bottom line, taking your educational program and packaging it online and/or as written material with video and audio available for the mobile society will set you apart from your competition and is the basis for your Pre and Post Surgery Program which you can charge for and mandate as you desire. You might think this additional charge will drive people away but in fact, it shows your dedication to their long term success and makes you unique. For surgeons that have a higher self-pay clientele, this is included in their package price and adds true value and even justification for their purchase.

3. **Establish counseling sessions/groups for accountability onsite, online or both:** What else goes with your packaged education? Often you already have counseling sessions and support groups you offer. As mentioned earlier, add these to the mix along with anything else you can think of such as fitness classes, a visit with your personal trainer, a promotional insulated water bottle or anything else you believe adds true value

An onsite monthly support group is a great idea and you likely already have this in place. I recommend adding an online private Facebook support group as well. Of course, this will require some monitoring by one or two of your staff members but it is a great way to keep your patients engaged and let them know about your great events and blogs.

Some surgeons are fearful of such a group due to potential liability issues. It is important to set 'rules' for the group to avoid such issues and to make sure your staff NEVER gives medical advice online. Rather, indicate for them to call the office or share that they will reach out to them that day (and follow-through on this promise). Your rules can be 'pinned' to the top of your page to re-direct such questions to the office. It is your decision but when monitored properly and expectations are set from the beginning, the online support group ends up being a great addition to your program.

4. **Package your materials/program in an easy to deploy membership site:** For the educational portion, you will likely want to offer it online as well. We have created programs in a variety of software programs such as Infusionsoft, Kajabi, ClickFunnels or the like. For access to a membership site comparison chart you can visit www.WeightLossPracticeBuilder.com/FreeResources.

It takes a bit of time to set it up along with a technology learning curve but it is something one of your staff can learn. Another option is to use the expertise of me and my team or others within those software communities. We even have a turn-key 12 month post-surgery program called Weight Management University for Weight Loss Surgery™ that you can license use of and we manage the tech for you. We can add your logo along with other customizations so delivery is personalized for you and your practice.

5. **Determine your price:** You have put together your package and now it is time to determine your price. Some factors to consider are what your market will tolerate (and don't underestimate this) and what you feel it is worth (covering all of your costs along with a profit). Each region is a bit different but I have seen pricing range anywhere from $199 to $999.

6. **Implement your program:** It's time to create some promotional materials, train your staff (who hopefully were

involved in the planning process) and launch it for all to see and get excited about. Your staff is typically the one who will share the benefits of the program and sell it to your patients. You are actually doing them a great service by having this together for them and in my experience, patient outcomes improve with education and accountability (counseling/support groups). Your staff will love having everything streamlined as well.

When sharing this with your patients, it is important to share the benefits, not just the features. They need to understand that there is no easier time than the first year after surgery to lose weight. However, surgery is just a tool and they need to understand how to optimize their new tool. They need to not only lose weight but change their habits as well for long-term success. This 12 month program will guide them each step of the way so they can not only lose weight but understand how to keep it off for life.

7. **Track patient engagement/outcomes:** Numbers matter. You just spent time creating a new program for your patients so you will want to track your numbers. Since the entire first year after surgery is critical, you will want to compare patient outcomes after the program has been in place for a year. In the meantime, you can track patient feedback and satisfaction.

Tracking numbers is the easiest part of this step. It is the engagement that poses the greatest challenge. Let's face it, people are busy and weight comes off pretty quickly the first year. Often your patients are doing so well, they don't think they really need you or your awesome comprehensive program (even if they paid for it already).

Engagement comes from knowing what interests your patients and delivering that (while sneaking in exactly what they need). Some engagement strategies that we have found to be very helpful include:

- Scales that communicate to you your patients weight
- Regular e-mails with educational videos, recipes and the like
- Educational social media posts particularly on Facebook and Pinterest
- Dynamic membership site that tracks progress through educational materials
- MP3 files for patients to listen to in the car
- Weekly podcasts that patients can listen to while walking/working out
- Engaging fitness videos with the surgeon, staff and/or personal trainers
- Unique fitness classes such as TRX, Strength Yoga, Barre and whatever is 'all the rage' at that particular moment in time along with certified instructors available to teach

8. **Modify as necessary:** Nothing is perfect, especially the first time around. And remember that 'done' is better than waiting

for 'perfect'. Make modifications to your educational program/ materials as necessary so they meet the changing needs of patients and remain fresh. The most difficult part of your pre/ post-op program is ensuring engagement. Therefore, communication with the patient is critical.

For example, we used to offer written modules for download on our membership site along with video and audio files. We also mailed the patient a module pertinent to that stage after surgery each month for an entire year with a DVD & CD. Over time, we eliminated mailing the DVD and CD but we still find our patients enjoy the membership site written, audio and video content, counseling, monthly events, monthly support groups, personal training visits and getting their module from us each and every month in the mail. All of these efforts help to keep them on track. It also keeps us top of mind which helps with long-term compliance (and retail sales) as well.

## Chapter 7:

# Profit Engine #3 – Cash Pay Surgery Profit Engine

The Cash Pay Surgery Profit Engine can help you increase your number of cash patients to 35-50% of your total surgeries and boost your profits by up to 40%. The Cash Pay Surgery Profit Engine and the Retail Profit Engine are by far, the two most impactful profit engines when it comes to your bottom line.

The Cash Pay Profit Engine is not only powerful, but one of the 5 profit engines that can bring the most enjoyment to you, your staff and your patients. Cash pay patients are easier to schedule and tend to be extremely motivated for success. And getting paid up front at a higher rate is enjoyable. If you structure your pricing well, your patients can end up with less out of pocket expense (and headaches) than they would have had going through traditional insurance plans. This seems to be a nice recurring theme – a win-win for everyone.

Surprisingly, many bariatric surgeons and especially hospital based programs tend to ignore the self-pay clientele. Like retail, it is generally not top of mind or a common service strategy they implement. However, with somewhat limited insurance coverage for weight loss surgery (with the exception of governmental policies), more and more people are researching their self-pay options...even if they have to leave the country for services.

Here is the process for implementing your Cash Pay Surgery Profit Engine:

1. **Adjust your mindset:** For many who are used to government and commercial insurances, attracting and working with cash pay patients can feel unusual and even a little scary. There are two mindset areas tend to need adjustment. First, the idea that it is okay to accept cash and to ask for this money up front. Second, being prepared for the concierge style care that goes along with cash pay patients.

   On the other side, I run into physicians who desperately want cash pay clients but aren't sure what to do to attract more of them and/or how to set up their cash pay program. They have adjusted their mindset but need the process and tools to make it happen. Hopefully these steps will provide an easy guide to follow.

2. **Determine your goals:** Evaluate what your current cash pay patient percentage of patients is and then determine by how much you want to increase it. If you want to transition exclusively to cash pay, it requires quite a bit of change/ planning but is well worth the effort. For those that want to test

the waters, your goal may be to increase your cash pay by 2% or perhaps 4 cases per month. This is also a worthwhile endeavor and an easier implementation plan.

Once you determine your goal, make sure you share it with key members of your team. Better yet, you may want to determine the goals together. Then you will want to use this formula to begin attracting these patients and meeting/exceeding your goal.

3. **Bundle all costs/track expenses:** Cost bundling generally includes a fee for the surgeon, the hospital, anesthesia and sometimes radiology (for any UGI testing) and cardiology (for pre-operative EKG) if they are independently owned. Look at your actual expenses, add your profit margin and estimate what your fee should be.

Meet with all parties involved and ensure that no one is adding unnecessary overhead that will price you out of the market. You may want to re-read that last sentence because it is all too common and will thwart your efforts.

Track your expenses for the past 12 months per patient. Then determine what your average reimbursement is from your primary payers. Are your costs being covered? For some payers, this may not be the case. Take your costs and compare it to your average reimbursement (for surgery and all visits pre and post-op up to 1 year after surgery). Take the higher of the two numbers and considering doubling the number for your self-pay rate.

I recommend including 12 months of visits and support so you will want to make sure that is covered. Your staff time for insurance approval, billing and collections will be minimal but those additional visits are necessary and can add up. Some consultants recommend determining your costs and adding a zero but for me, that doesn't always seem to be appropriate.

4. **Establish your package price:** You will want to do a market analysis for other self-pay programs in your area and negotiate a competitive package price that is acceptable to all parties. This is not a number you want to be constantly changing so make your decision carefully.

Go back to the number you determined in step #3 for your portion of the package price. Meet with the other parties involved and then see what you come up with as the global package price. Compare it to your market and adjust accordingly. You want to exceed expectations while being competitive in price. It would be great if I could just recommend a package price for everyone to follow but the reality is that different areas will tolerate different prices. Typically the highest portion goes to the hospital, then the surgeon, then anesthesia, then radiology and finally cardiology since they are usually just performing the pre-operative EKG.

Of course, your situation may be different. Everything is negotiable and once you determine your price, you will need to establish the benefits that make it worthwhile for your patients. This is what you will use in your marketing efforts.

If you offer insurance options for potential post-operative complications, you will want to make sure this is included in your package price or as an add-on benefit. This peace of mind option can also be a great marketing message.

5. **Define your ideal patients:** You will want to think about whom your ideal patients are that seek cash pay surgery. Who do you enjoy working with the most and where do they hang out? Your marketing messaging will need to be directed to them along with identifying their primary pain points (i.e. co-morbidities, lack of energy, diabetes) that prompts them to seek your treatment.

   Self-pay patients come with varied backgrounds and educational levels. If someone wants something bad enough, they are usually able to find the money to cover the cost from somewhere. Just as with insurance clientele, as the surgeon, you are the one who will determine if they are a good candidate for weight loss surgery. Co-morbidities become more of a concern sometimes if the patient is traveling to you/your program for services. You will find (depending upon where you are promoting your program) that you will potentially have more travel patients with a competitive package price, good reputation and comprehensive program.

6. **Create your marketing program:** Once you know your goals and your budget, your ideal patient and their pain points, you can create your messaging and how you want to deliver it. This doesn't have to be expensive. You want to build a relationship with them and then communicate your offer.

From experience, I can confirm that cash pay clientele are doing most of their research online. This is good news since online marketing is one of the most cost effective ways to market your services. Cost effective online marketing is usually the best way to reach this clientele.

As a caution, it is not recommended that you just place an ad on Facebook or on the internet touting your awesome program. Patients don't usually want to just hear about how wonderful *you* are. Rather, you will attract more patients if you address the benefits of weight loss surgery (the outcomes they seek). You may have heard the adage, *sell the shade – not the tree.* This is what you need to remember when putting together your advertising campaigns.

In my experience, Facebook is VERY particular when it comes to weight loss advertising. They want to ensure no false promises are being made and will usually not approve an ad with a before and after picture for that very reason. Be prepared for some ad denial before ad approval. Nonetheless, Facebook is a great way to reach your ideal patients and fairly simple to set up (and don't forget your retargeting pixels). The same is true for Pinterest and Instagram.

It is better if you are just sharing information about weight loss surgery or how it affects various problems like diabetes or hypertension. It is helpful to offer what is called a lead magnet as mentioned in Chapter 4. Your lead magnet offers helpful information in exchange for your prospective patients' name and e-mail. Then you can deliver this quality information and continue to provide them with valuable content via e-mail as you nurture your relationship with them. When they are ready, they will come in for a seminar or attend one of your online webinars. In the meantime, you continue to communicate with them and answer their questions.

If you build your relationship before you even meet, this increases the likelihood of follow-through and interest in YOUR services. As you know, follow-through with this clientele can be difficult. Your job is to remove the obstacles that keep them from improving their health, promote the benefits, provide them with options and then let them make their own decision regarding treatment.

7. **Monitor your positive ROI:** As I mentioned before, you want at least a 3:1 return on investment (ROI) with your marketing efforts. You will want to monitor your marketing spend and your direct results from these efforts. You may be used to measuring leads generated by the marketing effort which is important, but I like to track actual surgeries that result. This creates the true return on investment. You must take into consideration that the actual ROI is delayed due to a delay in follow-through and scheduling of surgery. However, it is possible to track this each month and that's what I generally recommend for your final ROI.

Managing costs is fairly easy because you can set spend limits on your online campaigns. This lets you test the waters and never end up with financial surprises.

If you are not getting a good result, it is generally your *message*, your *media* or whether or not you have put your message in front of the right *market*/audience. Refine, adjust and continue to monitor.

8. **Expand your reach:** Once you start to get traction, consider expanding your reach beyond your demographic area. As I mentioned, people will travel to get what they want. In those cases, it is then a matter of determining if they are a good travel candidate depending upon their overall health situation.

## Chapter 8:

# Profit Engine #4 – Incentivized Referral Program Profit Engine

I am often surprised by the number of surgeons/programs that do not have a referral program in place. Your patients are some of the most grateful people you will ever meet. They are grateful to you for the positive changes they now get to experience in their life. Many believe you saved their life and in many ways, you did! Let them send more people your way and be rewarded for their kindness and faith in you.

This profit engine is intended to help you double or triple your patient referrals without spending a dime on ads. And patient referrals are the best referrals. Here's how you can get more patient referrals in a way that makes you and your patient's look like rock stars.

1. **Adjust your mindset:** It can be uncomfortable to ask someone for a referral. Especially in the medical field. You will need to

adjust to the mindset that if your patient is happy, they likely want to help others feel happy as well. Your raving fans become your ambassadors and rewarding them for this is a great way to say thank you!

With each request, this becomes easier, especially when guided by your staff. Similar to the retail profit engine, patient referrals are best when requested and coordinated by your staff.

2. **Identify your ideal patients:** This seems like a recurring step for many of the profit engines. However, it's that important and a step that is often overlooked. With regards to your referral program, you will want to reach out to your best patient representatives. You want a variety of successful patients who will ultimately attract patients that can relate to them and their story. Thus, in addition to having literature about your referral program out in your office/exam rooms/restrooms, you will want to identify what patients you (your staff) wish to approach to share their story. Testimonials naturally occur when implementing your patient referral program.

I have found the best time for approaching weight loss surgery patients is when they are most ecstatic about their weight loss – usually at 6 months, 9 months and/or 1 year and are sharing their excitement with you. It is rare to have someone unwilling to do a written or video testimonial for you. Nearly all feel as if it is an honor. In fact, once your patients see all of the success stories of patients on your walls, they often get their feelings hurt if they are not asked to join the ranks of success with the other featured patients.

3. **Determine what they value most from you/your program and what you can afford:** When you are determining what your referral incentive will be (although an incentive is not mandatory), consider what your patients value most. Is it an additional counseling session? Is it a gift card to your store? Is it free passes to your fitness classes? You will want it to be something they value that isn't a huge expense for you. Is it a photo shoot where they get a free photo (many patients love this)?

   Your staff is one of your best resources for completing this step. They tend to know your patients extremely well and can see what they value. You can have a contest in the office for staff to come up with ideas and/or you can ask some of your seasoned patients directly. You have to be careful if you choose any apparel. If you choose to use apparel as a part of your referral program (such as a free t-shirt), you will need to be sure to stock all sizes. This is important because as you know, sizes vary not only among patients but a patient's size changes drastically as they quickly lose weight and you never want to offend them in any way with a shirt that is too large or too small.

4. **Create enticing/fun incentives for patient referrals:** Once you brainstorm what your patient's value most, determine what your incentive will be. For example, one of our offers for a comprehensive center is outlined so that when someone refers another person that has weight loss surgery (yes that is part of the criteria), they receive a $100 store gift card and then both they *and* the person they referred receive a free 6 month gym

membership at their office. The referrer also receives a free t-shirt making them an official part of their referral squad.

As another example, when someone refers another person and that person follows through with surgery, they a $100 store gift card and the person they referred gets a $50 store gift card. Or a manicure, or a pedicure, or a massage, or a free counseling visit...the reward options are only limited by your imagination. Again, if you run out of ideas, I am always here www.smarturl.it/bookkarol

5. **Establish an EASY system for referrals (and testimonials) to take place:** You will want to streamline the process for having information about your referral program available in your office, asking for referrals and tracking the referrals. This responsibility can be with one person or better yet, shared amongst staff. You just want to make sure everyone knows the process and that it is documented in your operations manual.

For example, one of our centers has one person who keeps up with creating/ordering all printed materials and one of their counselors has the conversation when she is meeting with the patient 6 and 9 months after surgery. That person also asks for a testimonial at the same time. Of course, if any staff member sees someone who would be a great testimonial, they take care of requesting the testimonial.

Asking for referrals and testimonials should be a spontaneous thing as people are sharing their success. You will find that the more your staff asks for referrals, the easier it becomes. The process often goes like this:

- Your patient stops into the store or the office for a visit

- Your patient weighs in and squeals with delight at the number

- Your staff member shares their excitement and congratulates them on their success.

- Your patient has their visit and while in the exam room, your staff congratulates them again and asks them if they are willing to share their story with others. If so, they have your patient sign a release form (of course), captures their story right then and there or gives them the testimonial form (1 page) and asks them to fill it out at that time or e-mail their response to the person who collects your testimonials. Of note, if they take the form home, the likeliness of completion is significantly lower. You will want to obtain it at that time if at all possible.

- Your staff member shares information about your awesome referral program and gives your patient some referral cards for them to give to carry with them and give to others who would like to look and feel as terrific as they do!

- Your staff creates the testimonial video or before and after graphic for you to post on your social media sites the next time "Patient Testimonial" is on your editorial calendar. I recommend posting one every 1-2 weeks.

All marketing materials for your referral program need to be easy to read with a clear call to action (CTA). You will want to make it as convenient as possible for them. Online, fax, e-mail, snail mail (with self-addressed stamped envelope) or other creative means.

At one year, most practices take an "after" picture of patients. The patients know this ahead of time so most will dress up and want to take a terrific picture. This is a great time to get their testimonial and remind them of your awesome referral program. Testimonials are a natural bridge to the referral program. You take their success and invite them to share it with others. They generally feel great about it and are likely to participate.

6. **Educate your team:** Once you determine your process, add the written process to your Operations Manual for staff and new hires to reference. Review the process at your next staff meeting and/or send out an e-mail with specific information to your team.

It's a great idea for managers or your lead person for the program to role model this process as an example for others. You can make it a fun role play at one of your staff meetings. I find that if you select someone (or have someone volunteer) to be the champion of the referral program, they will make it happen. They will be especially dedicated if they know the reason for the program and your goals. For example, your rationale is to grow your program and reward your best patients. Your goal might be to increase your patient referrals to 10 each month.

7. **Promote your program:** Create your fliers and announce it to your patients. Have it in exam rooms, patient bathrooms, at your support group meetings, in the gym and don't forget to share it on social media. These are all simple, inexpensive ways to promote something that will help your practice immensely now and in the future.

You can even utilize one of your referring patients to share their story about how they wanted to help someone they cared about get off their diabetic medicine and be able to be more active with their children. This is an alternative type of testimonial that increases awareness of your referral program and showcases your caring and successful patients. I have even recommended promotions with family members who have all had surgery talking about a referral program and/or their collective success. The more optimistic and fun you make the process, the more successful you will be.

8. **Track success/ROI:** Track how many patient referrals you are receiving. Monitor how smoothly the process is going. If your results are sub-optimal, don't despair. It is not usually your reward for making the referral (most will do this for nothing). It is usually something that needs to be marketed better or perhaps the way patients are being asked (or not being asked at all!). Change is hard and this is no different.

As I mentioned before, having a referral program champion in your office can make all the difference in the world. When people take responsibility, they will come up with creative ways to make things happen. You will generally find they will rise to the occasion and surpass your expectations.

## Chapter 9:

# Profit Engine #5 – Automated Marketing Program Profit Engine

I am not sure which profit engine is my favorite. I like them all! However, automation makes me extremely happy (almost giddy) and although I am a clinician at heart, I love marketing. This wasn't always the case. I used to despise marketing primarily because it seemed as if it was more expensive than it had to be and I almost always felt as if I was paying for mediocrity. I always felt like we were a number and never a priority for outside marketing companies. And then I learned automation...and everything changed!

I am one of those people who are always learning something new. This is particularly true when I am frustrated about something. I want to figure it out. Marketing seemed so elusive to me until I read many, many books and completed numerous courses, training events and certifications. I finally figured out how to make it work in the field of medicine, particularly bariatric surgery. It all goes back to what I shared in Chapter 4 (listed below). The beauty is that for potential patients investigating bariatric surgery online, step 1 and part of step 2 can actually be automated. The rest will be taken care of by you and your customer service oriented staff as these patients experience outstanding services and results – what you currently do each and every day.

1. Attract your ideal customers/patients

2. Build a quality relationship with them

3. Convert them to a weight loss surgery procedure or other services as appropriate

4. Turn these patients into Raving Fans that send more patients your way (and promote you to their PCP)

This profit engine is all about how you can create a steady stream of qualified patient leads and recurring revenue on autopilot. Does this sound too good to be true? I thought so too. That is until I experienced it firsthand.

The Automated Marketing Profit Engine may become your favorite as well because if done correctly, works 24/7 and can be monitored/updated easily by your trained staff – not you! Here are the steps for creating your very own (awesome) automated marketing profit engine:

1. **Identify what you want to automate:** What would you like to put on auto pilot? Getting contact information from potential patients (leads)? Product sales in your retail store? Patients for your online educational program? You are limited only by your imagination and if that's a problem, just give me a call!

Automated marketing brings people to you through your online message. You attract patients by sharing a message that resonates with a problem or frustration they are experiencing. You agitate that problem a bit and then share how you can help solve that problem. As I mentioned earlier (worth repeating), you don't just share how wonderful you are and try to sell them something. You haven't earned that sale yet. You need to sincerely understand their problem and share a valuable way to help them. At this point, it is best to stick with an educational resource or video that isn't overwhelming. Something they can easily digest and that piques their interest to know more about you and your services.

Most likely, you want to attract quality leads (patients) interested in weight loss surgery. So how can you automate this? Start by asking yourself what a common pain point is for someone seeking weight loss surgery? You are likely similar to me and have worked with these awesome people for a decade or two. They have pain points such as diabetes, hypertension, sleep apnea, desire to do things like ride rides at an amusement park, be active with their kids/grandkids, shop at a regular store, not require a seatbelt extender, tie their shoes and the list goes on and on.

You probably like to teach and can address many of these issues. I have a number of campaigns running online that offer a resource for how to eliminate diabetes. People read this report and then have the option of viewing a video from an experienced bariatric surgeon who shares how weight loss surgery can effectively cure Type II diabetes through rapid weight loss. At the end of the video, the person watching sees a call to action as to how to reach out to the surgeon's office. Qualified leads come into that office (day and night) about 3-5 times a week and 25% turn into surgeries. It can be challenging at first to set up, but with a little help you can be up and running in no time.

The sky is the limit in terms of what you can automate online. I have created content and helped set up campaigns for so many things such as weight loss surgery, medical weight loss programs, vitamins, back on track programs, weight loss nutraceuticals and numerous best-selling book campaigns for healthcare and business professionals (as a publisher). I say this not to tout such accomplishments but rather, to let you know that so much is possible and you don't have to be a graphic designer or trained online marketer to make it happen successfully.

Automation is great but let's face it – there are a lot of scams out there. I feel strongly that campaigns need to be true and ethical at all times. You need to be sensitive to the problems of others and share a genuine solution. This is the beginning of your relationship when you should be building trust, not hype and feelings of scarcity resulting in others feeling undue pressure. Patients trust you and they need to feel your sincerity from the very beginning.

2. **Create quarterly promotional plans:** Some people tackle their planning by creating a yearlong plan. This is great for a tentative plan but in reality, the world is ever changing and

working with quarterly promotional calendars can be more effective. I am going to share a number of options for implementation strategies you can include in your plan. However, please try not to get overwhelmed. Start with one strategy and add others if/when you need them.

For attracting new weight loss surgery patients, you will want to test a few campaigns and have the most successful running throughout the year (unless it begins to underperform). Each month, you can have blogs, testimonials and videos (if you desire) going out to nurture your community of patients. It is helpful if you are ready to respond quickly to any weight loss newsworthy happenings since this will reinforce your reputation as a valuable expert in the field of bariatric surgery and potentially attract new patients.

You can create a theme for each month and then coordinate your activities around that theme or topic. You can keep it interesting by incorporating special holidays with timely articles or recipes or both. As your confidence grows, you can test additional campaigns. If you are ever in need of ideas, we have the ability to send you ideas and campaigns as a handy monthly swipe file. There are also free resources available for you at www.WeightLossPracticeBuilder.com/FreeResources.

3. **Cross promote for existing patients:** Try to tie your promotions in with any blogs, podcasts, events or support group meetings you might be offering. For example, a blog on the importance of protein is a natural combination for promoting a protein product in your store. A podcast or post

about lack of energy is a great time to let people know about a B-Complex special you have going. An interview with one of your trainers is a great time to announce your latest fitness special.

Thus, it's a great idea to include various members of your team as you create your quarterly promotions. It's amazing how ideas can take flight when you have a creative team from your various cost centers brainstorming together.

I do want to caution that when you utilize products that are only prescribed by physicians, most companies forbid that you market them online to the general population. This is for a good reason – so that your patients aren't getting their supplements from someone else who is price cutting. They are careful to ensure that patients are purchasing from their surgeon and not random other corporations. You can still market them to your patients internally or via e-mail, you just can't put an ad out there on Facebook or try to have a sellers account on Amazon for these products.

4. **Systematize/assign ownership:** You and your management team can guide what you are creating and promoting but it is best to then let a staff member (or outside resource) run with it. Provide them with access to your automated Customer Relationship Marketing (CRM) e-mail system from either within your EMR system, external system or integrated into your retail store if you have one. You will also want to provide them with adequate training.

Some of my favorite software programs include Mindbody, Clickfunnels, Infusionsoft, Kajabi, ActiveCampaign, and LeadPages. Most of these systems can serve multiple functions such a landing pages, automated campaigns, e-stores and even membership sites. However, some just cover one or two of these functions. My team and I actively use each one of these listed currently for various businesses and clients. For more information about my favorite software systems, you can visit my website at: www.WeightLossPracticeBuilder.com/FreeResources

I used to think that I had to do it all. I wouldn't hand anything over to someone unless I knew how to do it myself. I wanted total control so that if someone wasn't available and the job had to get done then I could take care of it pronto! I thought this was actually a great way to manage because then everyone would know that I had their back! In reality, I was likely making my team crazy and preventing their professional growth by micro-managing a bit – okay, a lot!

Then came a day when I realized that I was spending so many hours at work and still having to complete what I didn't get done that night at home. Yet, I always had more on my 'to do list'. I felt guilty all of the time because I didn't have much quality time at home with my husband and 4 children. I was always thinking about the next campaign, article, automation resource, social media post and my mind didn't get much rest. I was exhausted. This also ended up in many unfinished projects and a great deal of frustration. Perhaps you can relate. Something had to give.

As I discuss in Chapter 12, it is critical for business success to surround yourself with a self-directed, smart, customer service oriented team. And this is what I had with a nearly zero turnover rate. So why didn't I let them do their job? That's when I began delegating and you know what happened? Exponential growth and project completion! I finally realized I had been holding progress back while thinking I was doing everyone a favor. Even better, I found that when I assigned ownership and attached to it the desired outcome, the end result surpassed my expectations. If you have a great team, your job isn't to try to do it all yourself, your job is to guide the vision and the desired outcomes, trust your staff and then sometimes – get out of the way.

5. **Track success:** Are you meeting your business outcomes identified for the month/quarter? Do you need to modify some of your efforts or do you need to add additional measures to those that are working pretty well? Do you and your team need to brainstorm new ideas? Is there disconnect between your message and what your patients want? These are the things you will want to take a look at and then make modifications. Once you have campaigns and systems working well, you can take a step back and get creative again for the next quarter!

6. **Rinse & Repeat:** Once you have a formula/template that is working pretty well, you can freshen it up but let it run. Once it has run its course, stop that marketing campaign and implement another. Now is the time you can also think about adding advanced marketing strategies such as split testing or expanding to add another social media option such as Pinterest

or Instagram. With a positive ROI, you may want to join some of our monthly campaign offerings or expand your services to include medical weight loss with one of our turn-key systems.

If you keep the needs of your ideal patient at the core of your marketing, you won't go wrong. Build sincere and positive relationships and let the referrals roll in as you expand your reach. Most important, make sure you are enjoying what you are doing. One of the reasons I developed these 5 profit engines and wrote this book was so I could help bariatric surgeons and hospital based programs expand their reach and enjoy the process along the way. I hope you have found this information helpful.

## Chapter 10:

## Putting it All Together

You have in your hands nearly 20 years' worth of research and implementation for building a successful bariatric surgery practice. I have not included additional aspects I have consulted on such as facility planning, strategic planning and financial planning, but I have included the top 5 engines that can make the quickest positive impact for you, your patients and your business.

It's up to you how you want to use the information. I recommend choosing one profit engine at a time and following the steps outlined for full integration into your practice. As I mentioned earlier, you may already have a robust retail store and would rather focus on self-pay patients. That is great! Use what is most helpful.

Sometimes people purchase a book such as this and read it for the information and get excited about implementation and then…do nothing. I implore you to take action. Remember, one person cannot do it all. Share this information with your team and develop your action plan together.

If you feel stuck, don't hesitate to schedule a 30 minute free strategy session with me at www.smarturl.it/bookkarol. I am also available for onsite evaluations as well as VIP weekend immersions for quicker implementation.

## Bonus Chapters:

## Chapter 11:

# Social Media that Supports Your Practice and Your Patients

Social media is a great way to promote your business, provide engagement and create more buzz. Using social media to create more buzz is something recommended for nearly all businesses – including your weight loss surgery practice. Think about it. People are 'connected' nearly all of their waking hours. Some people actually look at their phone just prior to bed and first thing when they wake up – even before they brush their teeth.

Never before has it been easier to be close to your ideal customers/ patients. However, it is also very noisy out there and it is difficult to get and keep their attention. This is where (as I have mentioned throughout the book) it is critical for you to understand who your ideal patient is, what their pain points are (what keeps them up at night) and where they hang out.

You can build your relationship through quality content and positive posts. In fact, I recommend 6 informational posts to ever 1 promotional post about your products or services. If you are viewed as the salesy one, it can be a total turn off and actually drive potential patients away.

I get asked frequently to set up and manage various business social media posts, online campaigns and e-mail marketing systems for clients. In fact, I could have a very lucrative business doing so and many national companied do just that. However, I believe that you shouldn't leave your online reputation to someone else. My team and I would rather teach you how to do it and provide you with quality monthly content and campaign ideas as desired so you ultimately have control over what is posted and when.

You will drive yourself crazy if you try to learn every social media platform at the same time. So don't do it! However, as you advance, you can get more of a bang for your buck by creating a post and then getting it out there on multiple platforms at the same time. In fact, there are some great services such as HootSuite (www.hootsuite.com) or IFTT (www.iftt.com) that will take your single post and distribute it across all of your social networking sites.

*You will drive yourself crazy if you try to learn every social media platform at the same time.*

There are other social media platforms such as Snapchat, Vine, Tumblr and Yelp. However, I have found that the top platforms for weight loss surgery practices include:

- Facebook (https://www.facebook.com) is the largest social site with over 2 billion users. This platform is familiar to most (especially males and females ages 35-54) and is used for socializing and building relationships (sound familiar?). People use Facebook to connect with others, to expose their brand and create customer engagement.

- Instagram (http://www.instagram.com) is primarily an image sharing platform for pictures and short videos. At the time this book was published, it was estimated that there are 800 million users on Instagram. This platform used to be dominated by teens but now attracts people in their 20's, 30's, 40's and beyond. Popularity for businesses continues to grow and studies have shown that 80% of Instagram users voluntarily connect with a brand.

- YouTube (http://youtube.com) If you want to see how popular YouTube can be for your practice visit www.youtube.com/docweightloss and you will see it in action for a robust bariatric surgery practice. YouTube is an online video hosting service. Some people don't think of it as a social networking site but with the ability to easily share videos and make comments (along with adding keywords for effective searches); this platform makes it very powerful for building your brand and sharing your knowledge. YouTube can also be set up to automatically feed to Twitter and Google+.

- Pinterest (http://pinterest.com) is dominated by women but likely your practice is dominated by women as well. This platform has been surprisingly effective at bringing in patients to many weight loss practices. This platform is all about images, especially photos and infographics. It has been shown that Pinterest users spend the most amount of money of any of the social media channels. This is a great place to share healthy recipes as well. Pinterest is where many of our website backlinks come from.

- Blogs (https://www.blogger.com or http://www.wordpress.org for free or self-hosted http://www.wordpress.com) are very popular for content sharing. In fact at least 25% of internet time is spent on blogs and social networks. Companies with blog have many more inbound links than those without blogs which can help with organic SEO. One of the things I love about blogs is that you can write the blog and then easily share it on your other social media platforms for additional links back to your site. You can do a standard written blog or use video, sometimes called a vlog. Below is a representation of what I mean.

- Twitter (http://www.twitter.com) is great for instant news and shorter conversations. Quite frankly, I have not seen this to be very helpful for bariatric surgeons other than to try to drive traffic to your website or to promote an online live event. Tweets have a short life so you need to repeat tweets to be most effective. However, Twitter does have your ideal demographic hanging out there – 65% females and typically 25-54 years of age. Twitter can be set up to automatically feed to Facebook or vice versa.

- LinkedIn (http://www.linkedin.com) is not only for getting your resume out there. It is known as the corporate, professional or employee site for social media. It is a professional site and I feel it is best utilized for business to business activities and interacting in professional groups of interest to you. Thus, not necessarily for obtaining new weight loss surgery patients.

- Google+ (http://googleplus.com) has grown in popularity. It is a social networking site offered by Google. It provides you with a way to do free video and communicate with one person or groups of people. Their primary audience is 18-34 year olds.

My top three choices if you are just starting out would be your Blog, Facebook and Pinterest. Each post you make should be created with your ideal patient in mind. Think about the topics they ask you the most questions about and begin there. To make it really easy for you, just answer those top questions in a blog post, share that to your Facebook page, make a great graphic that goes along with it and post on Pinterest. And by the way, if you have no idea how to create graphics, there are great programs out there for you to use. At the moment, my team and I like to use Canva, YouZign and Publisher.

You might be used to random posts because that's all you have time for. This may be easier but your results will improve if you actually schedule what you will post about (message), where you will post it (media), to whom you are trying to attract (market) and when (calendar). As discussed earlier, this is where your editorial calendar will come in handy to bring it all together. We prepare ours on a simple spreadsheet but if you search Social Media Calendars, you will find a plethora of ideas and examples. While writing this book, I did a search and found this resource quite helpful  https://blog.hootsuite.com/how-to-create-a-social-media-content-calendar/

For our clients that use online marketing effectively, they are finding on average 30% of their referrals find them online. This is amazing - You are getting new referrals as well as building your organic SEO rankings all at the same time. Now that's a beautiful thing!

As with any resource such as what I have provided here, none of it matters if you don't implement! And don't think it has to be perfect. Yes, your reputation is of utmost concern but social media is intended to be conversational. Creativity pays off here. You can get going in a few simple steps:

1. Decide which social media platforms you want to use and sign up for your free accounts.

2. Decide who is going to manage your posts.

3. Create your editorial calendar.

4. Implement your plan!

You are educating first and then promoting your services at about a 6:1 ratio. When it comes time for your promotion, you will want to be sure to have a clear call to action (CTA). Most social media platforms make it easy for you to offer your CTA which is where you will either have a lead magnet valuable enough for the person to enter their name and e-mail or you may be linking directly to an online educational product or a product from your retail store. The bottom line is to make sure your CTA doesn't get lost. You should only ask them to do one thing and then make that one thing is super easy to do.

For example, if you offered a 1 page infographic on the benefits of weight loss surgery and you want people to give you their name and e-mail prior to download, you don't want to take them to your main website page that is filled with a lot of other information. Rather you want to take them to a clean, professional landing page that has just one thing to do – show what they get and include a place near the top of the page for them to enter their information. Then they automatically see a simple thank you page and the resource is downloadable from that page or sent to their e-mail. I prefer e-mail because then they can confirm their e-mail (required) so you know they agree to future nurturing e-mails you will send. As you might have guessed, these future e-mails will include more valuable information you know they want/need and eventually information about your services in the event they are interested in making a purchase.

You can make social media as hard or as easy as you want. You won't know until you try. I believe that if you follow these simple instructions, you will be glad you took the plunge.

A word of caution: When creating graphics, only use your own photos (with permission if it includes patients) or royalty free photos. This is mandatory in order to keep you out of trouble. No larger corporation who monitors use of photos on the internet cares if you "accidentally" used the photo without permission or "didn't know". They will take legal action usually in the form of a fine and this is something you must avoid.

## Chapter 12:

# Keys to Effective Practice Management

We have a sign in the reception area that simply states "Happy to Be Here". I smile every time I see it because I am happy to be here. If I wasn't, it would be time to make a change. Fortunately, I think most of the team feels that way because we have a negligible staff turnover rate unless someone moves or are adversely affecting the operations of the office and/or quality of patient care.

Your office tends to have a 'vibe' (sometimes more officially referred to as your culture) that can be perceived by just about anyone who enters your office. Your 'vibe' begins at the top of your organization but can be influenced positively or negatively at any level. Remember earlier when you read that people buy based upon their feelings? Well your vibe is the feeling of your place of business. So it's important to pay attention to it.

What kind of vibe do you desire? Have you ever thought about it? If you haven't, I recommend you do. Especially if you are in a leadership position because you influence others perhaps more than you realize.

In our case, we enjoy a positive vibe that promotes respect, problem solving, teamwork, independent thoughts/ideas, creativity, caring, loyalty and determination to be your best. Now that's a lot!

I am not saying we are perfect at attaining all of these actions and have a perfect vibe each and every day, but it is something we strive towards. It is also an expectation for everyone no matter what position they hold. So how do you create such a seemingly elusive workplace vibe such as this? It is created by the people who work there and their relationships with each other and the customer (patient in this case). It is influenced by 3 things and we will break each of them down:

---

**Influencers of Your Business Vibe**

- Your Team

- Your Operations

- Your Wow Factor

---

**Your Team**

Your team is your greatest asset. You can have the most beautiful building in town, more money than you need, the most reputable physician or the best location around but if your team stinks (and I think you know what I mean), your overall success and reputation will suffer.

After effectively managing teams of 10-20 people in a physician office to teams with hundreds of people in a hospital setting, I believe the critical steps to building a team that supports your vision and is enjoyable to work with depends upon a few key strategies.

1. **Hire not only for the position but for the individual that will best serve the mission of your company.** I will relate this to bariatric surgery. If the position open is one for a physician or other clinician, you want to hire someone with experience in that area. You want to know their educational preparation/credentials along with their clinical experience. For everyone, you want to check references and complete a background check. However, if you are hiring for a medical receptionist, you want someone with experience but if they have the right customer service skills and good office/computer skills, often you can teach them the other specific operational skills.

2. **Understand your team and support their growth.** This is not only helpful for you but important for your team and surprisingly, many find it refreshing since not all leaders take the time to do this.

   At least once a year, you should meet with each staff member if possible to verify what is important to them in their job and inquire about their personal and professional goals. This can be combined with a performance appraisal if necessary. This will help you understand personality issues that may arise and also help you plan for appropriate advancement within the company depending upon their performance. We recently did this and found the following were most important to our medical receptionist and medical assistant staff. These are their direct responses:

- A good reputable physician

- Reliable CRM tool

- Knowledgeable, sales driven staff on program offerings

- Marketing campaign to get them in the door!

- Empathize, acknowledge and LISTEN to determine need – then direct appropriately

- Offer "welcoming support" make patient feel excited to be here; about themselves; and achieving their goals

- Research competition – offer a variety of options (THAT WORK) at varying price points for customer retention – "how we are better and why"

- Proactive, customer service and follow-up

- TEAMWORK…it makes the DREAM WORK!

- Organization

- Ability to multitask

- Compassion – along with this narrative – As a patient walks into a weight loss practice some are already feeling embarrassed, ashamed and even scared of the journey ahead. So compassion is something that everyone working in a weight loss practice should possess. Not only are we here to help the patient lose weight but we are here to help ease the patient into this life changing journey.

- A well planned friendly and positive environment

- Environment that makes our patients feel safe

- Appropriate accommodations for large patients

- Before and After Surgery Program that is educational and supportive

- Support (for staff) from physician/management

- Excellent communication

So what do you do with these? It is a great time to review with the physician(s) and management team to discuss if these are being addressed. When obtaining the list from each staff member, that is the time to review what can be improved upon and get their ideas. We expect that if someone comes with a concern or problem, they come with at least on solution for consideration. They rise to the occasion and make the entire process of quality improvement easier and more acceptable to all.

3. **Set clear expectations and communicate regularly.** Your staff wants to do a good job. However, if they are uninformed, they can be put in positions that compromise their ability to do so. Involve them in problem solving and make sure any operational changes are clear to everyone. Discussing any changes together and then following up with a written communication or a copy of the updated operational procedure tends to work well.

4. **Use staff meetings as 30% information and 70% discussion about processes that can be improved upon, new marketing ideas and teambuilding exercises.**

Meetings where you are just receiving information is helpful but in reality, can be quite boring. It almost seems like a dictatorship. Rather, discern what can be communicated via e-mail or other written means and spend your staff meetings to problem solve. I know you might be saying your team is too large or that will create mayhem but in reality, your staff wants to be a part of the solution. So let them.

To make it more controllable, you can set some ground rules so that one person doesn't dominate the discussion. You can set expectations that for anyone who identifies a problem, they need to present at least one solution. You can do team building at the meeting occasionally. All of these things tend to be more productive and contribute to a happier work place.

5. **Consider using employee position contracts that are signed by staff rather than job descriptions.** This improves compliance and an understanding of what the position entails. I recommend including the following areas: Expected Result, Tactical Work Expectations, Position Specific Standards and Companywide Standards (that are the same on all position contracts). If you want to read a great book in which a portion shares how to create position contracts, read *The E-Myth* and/or *The E-Myth Revisited* by Michael Gerber. These are great books for any entrepreneur.

6. **Make sure all staff understands their role as an ambassador for the physician and program.** Your staff members are the primary communicators with patients.

They can be the difference between patients feeling happy or disgruntled, feeling informed or confused. As my office manager recently put it – Patients should immediately feel confident that "We've got this" through specific system(s) that are in place to guide them through their weight loss journey – Start to Finish.

7. **Don't be afraid to discipline an employee who is not compliant with job standards.** You can counsel them and work with them to improve but sometimes you will do yourself (and the employee) a favor if you set them free (according to labor laws and HR policies of course).

8. **Don't tolerate poor customer service.** If you witness an employee demonstrating poor customer service, I recommend addressing it immediately in private. Poor customer service can be contagious and negatively impacts your reputation and your business. Document this behavior in the employee file and continue to monitor the situation. Some people might need additional training and/or mentoring. Provide such opportunities as appropriate. If the behavior continues, remember that everyone is replaceable. Document and counsel up to and including termination according to your Human Resource policies and standards. It's that important.

9. **Be honest and fair.** Enough said!

10. **Have integrity.** Being moral and ethical is not something you can necessarily teach. I believe integrity is behaving in congruence with what you internally know is right. Integrity is so important to me and I imagine to you as well. Being able to sleep at night knowing you have done the

right thing (even though it might not be the easy thing to do) is a great feeling.

11. **Reinforce that everyone on the team is marketing with each and every interaction.** This expectation needs to be set from the first day on the job. In healthcare, we rarely used to talk about marketing. We just talked about customer service and prompt resolution of complaints. The reality today is that most patients have a choice and while you don't need to operate on everyone who walks through your door (some obviously aren't good candidates); you do want to attract ideal candidates you enjoy working with. Everyone needs to understand that with every interaction patients have with your office, you are marketing/ promoting what you do. Having this mindset can be the difference between a thriving practice and one that is just getting by.

## Your Operations

Your operations refer to all of the processes you must have in place in order to run your program and create an exceptional customer experience. As I mentioned earlier, staff and patients alike crave consistency and order (whether they admit it or not). Having your processes documented helps with new employee orientation and cross training. Cross training is essential, particularly in a smaller program setting.

Operations also helps develop the standards that people are measured against. When a process changes, staff will appreciate knowing that before they have a patient standing in front of them. Remember, you (hopefully) have selected employees that want to do their best. Thus, your job is to provide them with the tools and guidance to do it the best way possible.

Of course at times there is a need for flexibility. But having a basic structure in place will keep your program/practice sane and leave fewer things up to chance.

**Your Wow Factor**

There has been a lot of discussion about what makes you different, what your 'vibe' is and what your customers want/need. Your Wow factor is what brings your vibe, your operations and your people (staff and patients) together. It is what you do as a leader and as an organization to add uniqueness and enjoyment to what you are doing each and every day. It is being able to take frustrations, figure them out and move forward in a better way. No program or person is perfect but if everyone understands the mission of your organization and the needs of your ideal patients it is easier to try to do the best job they can each and every day.

## Chapter 13:

# Karol's 7 Steps to Building a Successful Bariatric Surgery Program

As with any endeavor, building something new (or even renovating something older) tends to create various emotions such as excitement, fear, anticipation, confusion, stress, overwhelm and finally satisfaction, relief and pride when the project is complete. Fortunately, you can avoid most of the stress, overwhelm and fear with proper planning and by following an established process with proven results.

The process I am about to share with you for building a new bariatric surgery program or growing an existing bariatric surgery program is based upon experience and a LOT of trial and error (aka mistakes). Fortunately, I am an optimist and love a challenge. I am persistent and detail oriented (which can drive others crazy). So when a problem arises, as they always will, I work with our team creatively until we find a good solution. To my surprise and delight, often the solution ends up being better than the original plan.

Below are the 7 Steps to Building a Successful Bariatric Surgery Program (along with some personal advice for your consideration at the end).

### Step 1: Begin with the End in Mind

I am not sure if you are a Stephen Covey fan or not but his advice applies extremely well to creating your bariatric surgery program and life in general. Dr. Covey states that *Begin with the End in Mind* means to *begin* each day, task or project with a clear vision of your desired direction and destination and then continue by flexing your proactive muscles to make things happen.[15] This vision is what should drive your decisions and actions related to the design of your building/internal space, your furnishings, your décor, selection of your staff, patient population and services you offer to name a few. You may choose to visit other programs and see what they are doing but then it is important to make it your own vision with what you feel is the best of the best for what you want to create.

Don't be afraid to use your imagination and think about how you can use the present to prepare for the future. Many thought we were crazy to put medical, surgical, fitness and retail services under one roof. Actually we started to doubt the idea (well I did, Tom never had that thought) and yet, it has been duplicated in other cities and is now becoming the new standard.

Here is an example of what our vision entailed:

*We will create a comprehensive, state of the art weight loss center that includes adequate space for education, events, counseling, fitness, retail, staff support, exam/treatment and storage. The design will be non-traditional with an open, warm, 'groovy', unique, clean and organized yet inviting feel that showcases patient success. Our staff will be friendly, efficient, self-directed, optimistic, creative, skilled, dedicated, loyal and sensitive to patient needs. Our office and staff will support healthy habits with adherence to the same types of foods we encourage our patient to eat (of course special occasions excluded!). The staff will be rewarded for their dedication and have full access to the services we offer our patients in addition to products in the nutritional store available at cost. Our logo and brand will exude positivity, hope, success and a strong relationship with our patients. Communication will be clear and services offered in a concierge style. Our patient education will be thorough and available onsite as well as fully available on mobile devices for patient convenience.*

This vision drove our design decisions for an open style front desk, warm colors for décor, specific facility planning/design including some angled walls to enhance an open feel rather than a boxed look. There is soft lighting and sconces on the walls to create an elegant and yet comfortable feel. Chairs have no arms and match the décor along with classic/contemporary furniture in the waiting room/bathrooms and classroom. Table lamps and patient success stories adorn small spaces. Bright customized posters with professional patient photos and their quotes are placed strategically throughout the office on the walls. The computers all have wireless keypads and desks have little clutter. The fitness center has a private training area, access 5am-10pm and equipment that can accommodate the morbidly obese and challenging for persons of any size. The equipment is also easy to use with clear explanation and a video from one of the trainers available for each circuit machine. The floor is designed to absorb pressure and ease jarring of joints. On their own, the staff tends to have a protein shake for breakfast in the morning and follow primarily the same regimen as the patients. They are apt to share recipes they create and utilize the fitness center when they can.

Think about what you want for your center. The description above may sound overwhelming. Believe me, we have come a long way – we had a similar "feel" in our old building which was simply a renovated 7-11 building with terrible parking. Be creative with your space and make it something you are excited and proud to share with your patients.

If your plans involve new construction, select your builder carefully. Interview them and make sure if possible there is a foreman on site. This will help as you tour your new facility during construction and find things that require slight modifications or attention. Sometimes what is on the architectural plans looks a bit different once under construction.

## Step 2:  Create your Business Plan & Budget

Writing a thorough business plan is essential if you are seeking financing. It may also surprise your banker since I have been told that many businesses don't take the time to create a well written document that 'sells' your project. I can say that every bank we approached was willing to lend and it was primarily based upon our comprehensive business plan.

Key components of your business plan includes an executive summary, biography/curriculum vitae for the borrower(s), personal financial statement if you are the personal guarantor, personal tax documents and/or business tax documents for the previous 3 years, revenue history for the previous 3 years if available, projected start-up costs and projected profitability schedule for the next 3 years.

Even if you are not seeking financing, having an active business plan will help guide your decisions and goals. At the very minimum, you need to create a budget for any construction/start-up costs and a budget for your first year in business. Your budget needs to include at least your projected revenue (including major sources from various cost centers), minus your cost of goods sold (COGS) for net revenue. Then identify your direct and indirect expenses and subtract from our net revenue for your final projected profit/loss.

Sharing your financial goals with your staff is your decision. At the very least, they need to have volume goals and understand that they play a key role in the success of the business. This increases their buy in and commitment to meet or exceed the goals. Each and every employee is a critical cog in the wheel that determines if you travel smoothly or if your wheel breaks down and eventually crashes the car (your business).

My philosophy is that more information is better. I involve my management team in the initial annual/quarterly planning of volume and revenue goals. Then I fine tune these goals and they are shared with the staff. There have been times that we have used a profit share model but at the moment, they are rewarded with a bonus when the business meets/exceeds financial goals.

For the retail store, your staff needs to know exact revenue goals. You will find that they have a tendency to become obsessed with meeting or exceeding them. This is awesome! As a result, they may throw in a surprise special in order to drive sales. I used to direct all promotions and sales but soon found out that it is better to let them create the promotion and I just provide helpful brainstorming and approval. We have been doing this for a long time. Over the years, I have discovered that they tend do better when you get out of the way!

## Step 3:    Surround Yourself with GREAT People and Treat them Well

As you build your business, you will drive yourself crazy (and limit your success) if you try to do everything yourself. You must surround yourself with a competent, loyal, self-directed and motivated team. This includes your key employees along with your advisory team (corporate attorney, accountant, investment advisor, marketing specialist and coach/mentor). You may have a desire to cut corners here to save money. However, in the long run, you will actually spend more money due to staff turnover and potentially costly mistakes or "spinning your wheels" while getting nowhere fast. I say this from experience.

I am one of those people who like to figure everything out and do it myself because then I know it is done right (or so I thought). I used to micro-manage our team (which drove everyone crazy) and then I started to delegate…with trepidation.  Something I should have done a lot sooner. You see, I found that by micro-managing, I was limiting the creativity of our employees, discouraging them from problem solving, limiting their ability to grow and preventing myself from becoming a true leader. To make matters worse, I was spending little quality time at home with my husband and 4 children because I was so "busy". While the business was still doing quite well, another outcome was stagnation of business growth and less joy. I micro-managed because of my perfectionist personality and also because of fear...fear of losing control and discovering that someone else might do it better – crazy I know!

Once I trusted the wonderful team we had built and challenged them with desired outcomes instead of tasks, they rose to the occasion...and are much happier. They work hard and we reward them accordingly. This has afforded me the opportunity to build my consulting business along with 2 additional businesses. I can actually relax knowing that processes and people are in place to keep the center moving in the right direction with a focus on stability and growth along with above average patient outcomes and satisfaction.

So how do you build your dream team? This comes from your hiring process and your commitment to the fact that "everyone is replaceable". I am not cold hearted and actually we have a negligible turnover rate. If a position opens up it is usually for one of three reasons: someone is moving, someone has been nurtured through the practice to move beyond their role and has advanced to a new job (more on this later) or they aren't a good fit (which preferably needs to be discovered during their orientation phase). Of course we follow employment rules and regulations, but we aren't afraid to document and discipline up to and including discharge if necessary. Fortunately, these instances are few and far between.

If you are in a large healthcare system and do not have a choice in your employee selection, I would challenge the precedent. Your staff is that important! As you know, they are your representative. They are your first impression on many occasions. They are the ones who can prevent or instigate an unhappy patient. They are critical to an office that is enjoyable and an office that is productive (or not).

Where you find great employees varies. In my experience, I have found my best employees via word of mouth. On occasion I have found a great employee through an online advertisement but never through a temp agency. However, your experience may be different. Fortunately, I have a number of employees who have been with Tom since he moved to the area 23 years ago. They are that loyal, reliable and awesome.

Other important aspects to building a great team include:

- Take the time to meet with your staff and find out what their long term goals are. If possible, you should help them grow and support their further education. If you are a new manager to a practice, this is a great way to get to know your staff better and let them know you are interested and care.

- Make sure you complete employee performance appraisals. This is a great time for you to share what is going well and what may need improvement along with determining goals for the next year. I will have staff fill out a questionnaire before we meet so I can see where they feel their strengths lie, where there areas for improvement and what goals they have for themselves personally or professionally. Often you will find they are ready to take on additional responsibilities and this is a great way to help them grow and perhaps take a burden off of yourself or assist with a new project you have been thinking about.

- Always be fair. Playing favorites will get you into trouble and undermine staff respect for you.

- Follow through on what you say you will do. People need to know they can trust you.

- Find ways to recognize and reward your staff. A thank you verbally or with a personal note means more than you know. Remembering birthdays is also a nice touch as well as staff employment anniversaries.

- Team build in creative ways whether it is a quick game at work, "Spooking" them with candy at Halloween, a Christmas celebration or running a 5K together. These activities go a long way. It is fun to also create photos you can post on Facebook. This actually increases engagement with patients.

- We actually create job contracts for each position that the employee needs to sign. It is a job description that is written as a contract and requires a signature. It mandates a review of responsibilities and reinforces the importance of following through each and every one.

As you know by now, your team is critical. They can make the difference between great days at work and days you got nothing done because you felt like you were babysitting teens or toddlers. Your example goes a long way. Be kind, be consistent, be firm when necessary and don't forget to say thank you.

## Step 4: Build Systems

Systems create calm from chaos and provide consistency that patients and staff both appreciate. Effective systems also create predictability for your business and extra time for you. You need them!

The top systems that need to be in place include: scheduling (patient & staff), clinical documentation, patient education, retail sales, marketing, financial, patient outcome tracking, EMR, billing & collections, patient testimonials and office patient flow for each practitioner.

Systems simply mean that you have an organized set of procedures in place that can be easily performed to create predictable outcomes and utilized for staff training as necessary. These systems need to be documented and updated regularly. I find it is easiest to review them at the end of the year and anytime throughout the year when your 'flow' is disrupted which is usually caused by the constant of change. No need to take this on alone. Your staff is the best one to document what they do each day.

## Step 5:  Obtain Center of Excellence Designation

How to obtain your Bariatric Center of Excellence (COE) designation is beyond the scope of this training. However, it is important. If you aren't already a designated COE, more information is available at https://www.facs.org/quality-programs/mbsaqip/apply

The top accreditation for a Bariatric Center of Excellence is obtained through the American College of Surgeons. *"The program accredits inpatient and outpatient bariatric surgery centers in the United States and Canada that have undergone an independent, voluntary, and rigorous peer evaluation in accordance with nationally recognized bariatric surgical standards. Bariatric surgery accreditation not only promotes uniform standard benchmarks, but also supports continuous quality improvement.* "[16]

Accreditation is very worthwhile. It involves quite a bit of preparation and ongoing data entry but you will set yourself apart from other non-accredited programs and have access to their large database for national standards and benchmarks. It also helps from a marketing standpoint for your credibility and commitment to excellence.

## Step 6: Market Your Program & Measure Results

I hope by now you understand not only how important marketing is but how you can simplify the process for maximum results. We reviewed the top marketing strategies for your bariatric program along with information on automation in the Automated Marketing Profit Engine portion of the training.

There is no reason for you to perform random acts of marketing any longer. Once you have your marketing campaigns and promotions lined up for each quarter, you can tweak them as necessary and put them on auto pilot. Hopefully, you understand how you can deploy a new one as necessary. Finally, if you have a retail store, this is your ticket to getting in front of your customers and patients each and every week with a sales e-mail that also includes education to help them understand how to be successful.

You and your staff are actually marketing all of the time whether you realize it or not. Taking great care of your patients, monitoring when they are feeling particularly successful and happy and capturing that moment in a photo or video to share with the world (and more patients like them), creating engaging posts for social media, posting recipes on Pinterest, following your editorial calendar, creating blogs, educational materials, podcasts, webinars, visiting referring physician offices, asking for a referral, obtaining a testimonial and the list goes on and on. It becomes so second nature and fun that you don't even realize you are doing it (well you do but often the staff just do it because they enjoy it). Share, share, share so your ubiquity footprint grows and more people can find you online and around town.

## Step 7:  Implement Growth Strategies

Growth strategies include implementing everything that was outlined in the 5 profit engines. If you want to grow, your strategies are outlined there. The critical difference between programs that grow and those that stagnate or disappear altogether is that the growing program is engaged with their prospective patients as well as their current patients. They have a relationship with them that naturally creates a buzz and additional patients coming through the door.

Implement what you have learned here and you will be on your way to growth. If you need help, send me a note at Karol@WeightLossPracticeBuilder.com It really is easier than you think!

Now to the unsolicited advice I promised you. I couldn't help but share a few other suggestions that aren't mandates but will result in more enjoyment for you in your personal and professional life. As an extension, it could make a difference for your staff and patients as well...not to mention your family. Enjoy!

## Have a Passion for What You Do

There is no denying the fact that if you love what you do, you are happier and much more effective. It doesn't even feel like 'work'.

Rather your passion creates joy, motivation and positive outcomes with faster results. This may sound a little surreal or unrealistic but it is so true! You can't fake passion. When you are passionate, your actions are much more believable and inspirational. This is especially true when it comes to building a successful weight loss practice.

Let's face it, weight loss is hard! So having a practitioner that is passionate about helping others lose weight and improve their health is very important. If it's not you, don't stress it – the passion can also come from your physician extenders and staff. This passion (and overall vibe) will differentiate you from others who may be building a weight loss business for the wrong reasons.

**Practice What You Preach**

It is easiest to coach people to success when you are successful yourself. It also feels congruent when your personal values match your professional values and goals. This can bring extreme enjoyment and peace. I am not saying you need to be perfect or even close to perfect, but I am saying that you should try to walk the talk and practice what you preach.

You wouldn't seek financial advice from a company that just went bankrupt just as you wouldn't likely seek health advice from someone who isn't somewhat healthy themselves. There is the thought that misery loves company and if your practitioner is "in the same boat" they will better understand, but that's not the way to the path of improvement.

Similarly, in any sport, it is better to play with those more skilled than you – that's how your game improves and how you challenge yourself to get to the next level. Another natural outcome is that your level of accountability for your own health usually becomes more intense when you are providing weight loss services. As a result, you are healthier, happier, driven and more creative. When you feel your best, you tend to bring out the best in others. Positivity and great results are contagious!

## Be Intentional

We are creatures of habit and usually don't like change. So often you may go about your day doing the same things even though your actions aren't creating the outcome you desire. You may feel stuck and simply used to doing things the way you always did them. And frankly, that feels comfortable and safe.

You also are extremely busy or overwhelmed and taking time to really think about what you want personally and professionally isn't possible with your schedule. Or so you believe…

No one can do this for you but it is critical to your success and happiness. If you don't know where you are going, you can't be intentional about your day to day activities and before you know it, years have passed by and you just continue to be in the same rut. And one day, you may regret not pursuing what you really want and deserve.

Believe me, I fought this for a long time and wouldn't have succeeded in building a number of successful businesses unless I got over my fears and reasons for procrastination. I also worked with a coach to help me break out of my rut and create my vision. In addition, I shared this with my husband. He is a great sounding board and helps to support my vision/actions. This method also works for our children as well. We like to break it down this way:

1. 3 Year Vision – My 'Why' or motivation. I describe exactly what my life will look like in 3 years from a personal and professional perspective. I write this in present tense as if it is 3 years from now.

2. 1 Year Goals – My 'What' I have accomplished over the next year. I write this in present tense as if it is one year from now.

3. 90 Day Strategy – My 'How' to accomplish my goals. I list my 'Top 3 Projects' along with the most important 4-8 actions that will get me where I want to go.

4. This Week's Actions – My 'Now' actions that relate to my 90 day strategy. I revise this weekly and then make sure the actions are incorporated into my schedule that week.

I document this in one table with 4 boxes and keep it in front of me each day to keep me focused and 'Intentional'. This is key for me because if my actions are intentional (deliberate, conscious, done on purpose), I see progress. Otherwise, I let others drive my schedule by constantly volunteering, putting fires out and being 'busy' instead of accomplishing my weekly actions…which contribute to my top 3 projects…which lead me to attaining my goals…and living the life I envision and desire.

## Don't Be Afraid to Add a Retail Store

I used to think retail felt a bit weird. We are healthcare providers and the thought of sales felt terrible. We dabbled with a very small store (literally in a closet) and soon I realized that the products we carefully selected actually improved patient outcomes. I discovered that they loved having products available to them and that our retail store helps to build a stronger relationship since it keeps them coming back. Believe it or not, our retail store generates $480.000+ gross revenue each year.

And, once you have a wonderful retail manager (again surrounding myself with great people) with systems in place you don't have to be the salesperson. Retail doesn't have to feel salesy. You are actually helping your patients get better results and adding another revenue stream into your practice.

## Learn from Your Experiences (success & failures alike)

Just like long term weight loss, business success and life is a journey that is experienced minute to minute and day to day. We need to take it one day at a time and learn to enjoy it more.

In your program, you will experience success and failures. These lay the foundation for positive growth – if you let them. We view failures as a learning experience and then we move on. I encourage you to do the same.

Learning from your past can be hard to do. You may think your past defines who you are today. The reality is that your past does not predict your future. Only you have control over your destiny.

## About the Author

**Karol H. Clark** is a best-selling author, speaker and entrepreneur who has a passion for helping physicians integrate effective, profitable weight loss services and retail sales into their practice while improving patient outcomes and enjoying the journey along the way. Her use of non-traditional (easy to implement) medical marketing strategies, along with her dedication to a positive ROI makes her a uniquely different and sought after weight loss business and publishing consultant.

Karol is formally trained as masters prepared Registered Nurse in the field of women's health, medical and surgical weight loss, and nutrition. She is also a marketing expert with over 20 years of experience as a hospital administrator, surgical practice administrator, and coach.

Karol is a certified professional with Author Expert Marketing Machines, Make Market Launch and Publish & Profit. She lives in Virginia with her husband and their four children.

Karol can be reached at Karol@WeightLossPracticeBuilder.com. You can also visit her business sites at www.CFWLS.com, www.WeightLossPracticeBuilder.com, www.YourBestSellerBook.com and www.CenterforHormoneHealthandWellness.com.

If you would like a FREE business strategy session, sign up at www.smarturl.it/bookkarol

# References

[1] http://connect.asmbs.org/may-2014-bariatric-surgery-growth.html

[2] http://asmbs.org/patients/benefits-of-bariatric-surgery

[3] https://obesitymedicine.org/why-is-obesity-a-disease/

[4] http://asmbs.org/resources/approved-procedures

[5] http://connect.asmbs.ort/may-2014-bariatric-surgery-growth.html

[6] http://www.obesityaction.org/educational-resources/resource-articles-2/weight-loss-surgery/dear-doctor-ive-had-bariatric-surgery-will-i-ever-get-to-normal-weight

[7] https://asmbs.org/resources/sleeve-gastrectomy-as-a-bariatric-procedure

[8] http://scribeamerica.com/blog/physician-reimbursement-why-it-matters-for-the-future-of-american-health-care/

[9] Medtronic 2017 Bariatric Surgery Medicare Reimbursement Coding Guide, January, 2017

[10] http://www.ncsl.org/research/health/health-insurance-premiums.aspx

[11] https://www.obesitycoverage.com/before-paying-cash-for-bariatric-surgery-read-this/

[12] https://www.healthcarecommunication.com/Main/Articles/How_patient_expectations_for_health_care_providers_9609.aspx

[13] https://en.wikipedia.org/wiki/Concierge_medicine

[14] https://12weekyear.com/

[15] https://www.stephencovey.com/7habits/7habits-habit2.php

[16] https://www.facs.org/quality-programs/mbsaqip/about

Made in the USA
Columbia, SC
10 October 2017